EXETER

THE BLITZ AND REBIRTH OF THE CITY

The Reconstruction of the Central Areas of Exeter
1945 – 65

Norman Venning

DEVON BOOKS

First published in Great Britain in 1988 by Devon Books

Copyright © Jean Venning, 1988

Illustrations © Exeter City Council (except where indicated otherwise)

ISBN 0 86114–830–4

British Library Cataloguing-in-Publication Data
Venning, Norman
    The reconstruction of the central areas of Exeter 1945-65.
    1. Devon. Exeter. Inner areas. Redevelopment 1945-1965.
    I. Title
    711'.4'094'0942356

Printed and bound in Great Britain by A. Wheaton & Co. Ltd

DEVON BOOKS

Official Publisher to Devon County Council
An imprint of Wheaton Publishers Ltd, a member of Maxwell Pergamon Publishing Corporation plc

Wheaton Publishers Ltd
Hennock Road, Marsh Barton, Exeter, Devon EX2 8RP
Tel: 0392 74121; Telex 42794 (WHEATN G)

SALES
Direct sales enquiries to Devon Books at the address above.

Trade sales to: Town & Country Books, P.O. Box 31, Newton Abbot,
Devon TQ12 5XH. Tel: 08047 2541

CONTENTS

ACKNOWLEDGEMENTS

The illustrations included in this narrative have been taken from various sources.

I am grateful to the Express & Echo, the Western Times Co. Ltd and to the Exeter City Council for the excellent photographs. Such other photographic reproductions, where appropriate, have been extracted from Exeter Phoenix, the Municipal Journal, Devon Life or City Council publications. Maps and plans are based on the Ordnance Survey Maps, to which Department acknowledgement is made. As regards the text, the majority of it is based on my own personal notes and memory and on Reports made during my career in the City Engineer & Surveyor's Department. Certain notes on the air raids were based on information obtained from the Sunday Independent newspaper. Finally, I express my grateful thanks to my daughter Caroline for her help and patient typing of my scrappy and often illegible manuscripts.

The publishers would also like to thank Mrs Venning, the author's widow, and Mr Brierley, the previous City Engineer who retired in May 1972, for their help in the production of this book.

Maps have been redrawn and labelled by Ian Foulis and Associates.
Illustrations on pp. 91 and 92 are by Jim Lester.

The photographs on pp. 11, 13, 14, 93, 94 and 96 are reproduced by courtesy of Isca Historical Photographic Collection.

LIST OF ILLUSTRATIONS

LIST OF ILLUSTRATIONS

AUTHOR'S PREFACE

In writing this narrative I have tried to record a factual account of the work of reconstruction as seen by myself, as one engaged from 1945 to 1974 in the service of Exeter City Council.

Some criticism has been raised regarding the redevelopment as to desecration, lack of foresight, or the need for conservation, etc. and I do not set out to answer or defend these criticisms. As an officer of the Council, one carries out one's duties as determined at higher levels, regardless of political shades and personal preferences.

Further criticism may be levelled at the formation of main traffic routes through shopping areas, or the lack of elegance in building designs. Nevertheless, it is hoped that the description of events from 1945 to 1965 will prove to be an interesting account of Exeter's struggle to its feet following the Second World War.

Finally, I must apologize if this account is angled more from a road-construction angle than from a building one. The reason is that my personal experience has been gathered from work in the City Engineer's Department and I have found much satisfaction and contentment in working for thirty years amongst all sections of the departments of the old City Council.

ABOUT THE AUTHOR

Norman Venning was born in Plymouth in 1914 and educated at Plymouth College and Wycliffe College in Gloucestershire.

A Chartered Civil Engineer and a Member of the Institution of Civil Engineers, he joined the staff of Exeter City Council at the end of 1945, where he was closely involved in the redevelopment of the city after the war. He remained in the City Engineer's Department until 1974 when he retired.

This book was written during his retirement, with no thought of publication. He died in 1983.

FOREWORD

The manuscript of Norman Venning's personal account of the rebuilding of Exeter after the last war was presented to the City Council in May 1977.

It is particularly relevant that an illustrated record of the 'rebirth' of Exeter should be published at this time when many of the areas described in the book are themselves now subject to pressures for change and redevelopment.

I am therefore very pleased to be associated with the launch of Norman Venning's book and the part played by The City Council in ensuring its publication.

INTRODUCTION

The programme of development of the city's new street layout is outlined in the following pages. It will be evident that the fifteen years from 1950 to 1965 were years of great activity. One could say that possibly never before in its history had such intense development taken place in Exeter. This was of course largely due to the need to get the city back on its feet again as soon as possible, and government grants to this end enabled this to proceed with the greatest speed.

Indeed, cities that had not yet prepared schemes or received government approvals for their redevelopment schemes were naturally further back in the queue, and such funds as were then available were directed towards those towns and cities which already had new plans prepared and approved.

Exeter, fortunately, based its new layout on the lines that existed, for the most part, before the war and shopping streets were to be perpetuated in locations where previous generations had established them.

After the cessation of hostilities in 1945 there lay ahead the tremendous task of rebuilding the city's commercial centre, the restoration of trade and industry and the need to provide housing. This, together with the demobilization of thousands of men and women from the services, underlined the need for a speedy commencement of rebuilding.

The devastating air raids on the city in April 1942 — and particularly the blitz on the night of 3 – 4 May 1942 — had caused grievous damage to the central shopping and business areas, besides damage and destruction to residential and industrial premises. By 1945, however, some measure of orderliness had been established by the demolition of ruined walls of buildings, the random filling of basements and general clearance work. It was thus possible to look across the devastated areas where the extent of desecration was at once evident.

There were three main areas of devastation in the centre of the city:

(a) **High Street area** — from Eastgate (Debenhams) to St Stephen's Church (Dingles) and from the City Library (ruined) to Southernhay West.

(b) **Fore Street/South Street area** — from Mary Arches Street to Coombe Street and from the Cathedral precinct to Market Street.

(c) **Sidwell Street area** — from St Sidwell's Church to The Triangle car park, Clifton Road, and from Belmont Road to approximately the site of the present-day Homesense.

PART 1

ONE

High Street Area: Condition in 1945

High Street Area: Condition in 1945

The High Street area was the first to be dealt with. Reconstruction of Fore Street and Sidwell Street areas followed later as government funds and approvals to layouts were granted. It is therefore as well to record the condition of this area first and in greater detail.

The existing road pattern could readily be seen, for one could look from the City Library site across High Street to the old City Wall at Southernhay West and from Eastgate to the backs of the buildings in the Cathedral Close.

The area was generally flat, save for stray weeds or Buddleia plants growing among the stones or the occasional solid concrete floor platforms that indicated the presence of former buildings. Such floors were those of The Commercial Union and Burton's, fronting High Street; the old Bluecoat School, where the present Princesshay arcade to Post Office Street now exists; the floors of the old Deller's Cafe and Lloyds Bank, abutting Catherine Street and Bedford Street respectively; and there were, of course, others.

It was a bleak, draughty, desolate area and, as one walked along this section of High Street, there were displayed on the various bombed sites notice-boards indicating the name of the firm that formerly stood there and, if they were trading elsewhere, their new address. These were rather reminiscent of silent tombstones.

The ground floor of Westminster Bank still stood at the corner of Castle Street/High Street where indeed it stands today, in new form and abutting a considerably wider Castle Street.

Barclays old bank premises on the north side of old Bedford Street still remained standing with damaged upper floors. This was later to be rebuilt in an adjacent building.

That portion of the telephone exchange abutting Castle Street and New Buildings Lane remained standing, though its extension towards the new City Library was to follow later.

In the centre of the area that is now crossed by Princesshay arcade

1945. Looking west across High Street (Old Kings Alley bath seen behind the bank)

1945. Looking south across High Street (Old Bampfylde Street in line with Cathedral)

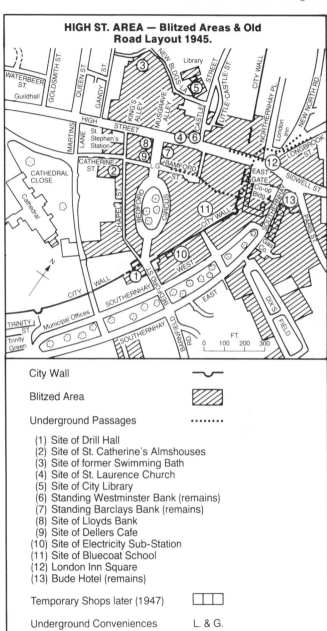

south of the old one. This was so that the new road could be constructed while the old was still in use. Bedford Circus, with its famous oval green

HIGH ST. AREA — Blitzed Areas & Old Road Layout 1945.

City Wall	⌄
Blitzed Area	▨
Underground Passages	········

(1) Site of Drill Hall
(2) Site of St. Catherine's Almshouses
(3) Site of former Swimming Bath
(4) Site of St. Laurence Church
(5) Site of City Library
(6) Standing Westminster Bank (remains)
(7) Standing Barclays Bank (remains)
(8) Site of Lloyds Bank
(9) Site of Dellers Cafe
(10) Site of Electricity Sub-Station
(11) Site of Bluecoat School
(12) London Inn Square
(13) Bude Hotel (remains)

Temporary Shops later (1947)	☐☐☐
Underground Conveniences	L. & G.

were the traces of the former Bluecoat School, as mentioned earlier, and Bedford Garage which was later, during the reconstruction, to be resited at Summerland Street/Western Way.

In the old Bedford Street were underground conveniences. The gentlemen's was situated on an island site in the centre of the carriageway between Catherine Street and High Street. The ladies' was near the northern tip of the oval green of Bedford Circus. Both of these were later to be demolished and substituted by new underground conveniences in Catherine Street adjacent to St Stephen's Church.

Car parking was no problem. It was quite possible for cars to mount the kerb and park anywhere the drivers liked. In Bedford Street vehicles parked around the outer perimeter of the oval with some rough semblance of order, though there were, of course, no markings. It will be appreciated, of course, that traffic in 1947 was nothing like it is at the present time.

Beyond the City Wall at Southernhay West two long, lofty terrace blocks had been destroyed. These buildings, similar to the Georgian terraces further down Southernhay West, had comprised offices with some residential premises as well. Likewise in nearby Dix's Field fire had gutted two opposing Georgian blocks separated by a green and accessible through a small opening off Southernhay East: a classic piece of architectural grouping. The site in Southernhay West is now occupied by Broadwalk House. At this time, however, the site was barren, with low-lying overgrown gardens, damaged party walls and semi-filled basements.

The Old Road Pattern

The cleared area of High Street enabled one easily to pick out the old street layout. High Street and Bedford Street were similar in location to their routes today, though the new Bedford Street is a street's width to the

Fore Street, facing North Street, 1942

Catherine Street, 1942

and large trees in the centre, was a striking feature and was sited where the Head Post Office (main entrance) now is.

Running off Bedford Street and in line with Catherine Street was a very narrow roadway called Bampfylde Street. This street name is perpetuated in the later-constructed road abutting the Coach and Bus Station, Paris Street. This street was as narrow as Catherine Street near St Martin's Church. It turned left at a right-angle to join High Street opposite Castle Street (i.e. where the present arcade exists).

Castle Street itself was as narrow as that section opposite the telephone exchange and Little Castle Street extended further down towards High Street before merging into Castle Street itself.

The present shoring supporting the flank of the last remaining building in Castle Street bears evidence that in fact some buildings had to be removed to allow the service road (Bailey Street) to emerge on to Castle Street at a later date.

There were some narrow courts or alleys leading off High Street, the main street. These were passages that ran beneath the buildings fronting High Street. They opened out at the rear to serve either a few small cottages or perhaps a large house. A street lamp (gas) often lighted these passages, particularly where they were registered as a public highway, being repairable 'by the public at large'.

In High Street, on the north side, such passages as Watts Court, King's Alley and Musgrave Alley were well known. King's Alley led to the site of a swimming bath located in the vicinity of the present toilets in Musgrave Row. Musgrave Row derived its name from Musgrave Alley which, in turn, was named from Musgrave House to which the alley gave access. Musgrave House was a large house with garden situated on the site of what is now Musgrave Row. It was occupied by a Dr William Musgrave who died in 1721.

At Eastgate, where the Co-operative Society premises had miraculously escaped destruction while all around had been laid low, there was a junction of six converging roads. These were: Northernhay Place (off High Street) and Longbrook Street (both feeding into London Inn Square), Sidwell Street, Paris Street, Southernhay and High Street. In the new layout this junction was to be simplified to a four-way crossroads by the diversion of Northernhay Place into New North Road and by realigning Paris Street so that Southernhay joined Paris Street lower down, rather than at Eastgate. At Eastgate, as in some other places, a basement of an old shop had been converted into a static water tank. Other surface tanks had also been suitably sited for fire-fighting in the war. These were gradually being eliminated.

The Plan for Exeter, 1945

The first thing the City Council did was to engage a professional town planner to make a study of Exeter, its population and movement, habits, business and trade potential, etc., with a view to drawing up a viable plan for the city. Thus it was that Thomas Sharp came to Exeter. He, together with other planners, was engaged in preparing similar plans for other blitzed towns and cities in the country.

Thomas Sharp stayed in Exeter in 1945 for a number of weeks to make his investigations and collect the data in support of his projected plan for the city. He stayed long enough to get the 'feel' of the atmosphere of a cathedral city.

He studied the records of retail and distributive trades, farming, and movement of population from outlying areas that came into the city for work or leisure. The needs of industry and existing use of land and premises were also recorded.

These facts and figures were produced and pubished in a book called *Exeter Phoenix* which was illustrated by plans and drawings and showed Sharp's proposals for rebuilding the city.

An exhibition of his plans and drawings were prepared in the shell of the old City Library building. This building was badly damaged by fire in the raids but the erection of screens around the walls and the provision of fluorescent lighting fitted out the exhibition, whose centrepiece was a scale model of the central area of the city. The exhibition was opened in 1946 and thereafter was thrown open to the public. Conducted parties visited the exhibition and were given a detailed explanation.

Sharp's proposed central redevelopment plan
(Left) *1949. Work in Princesshay. Temporary shops in the background*

Details of Sharp's Plan for Exeter

The streets of Exeter were narrow and many examples of medieval or pseudo-medieval buildings were still in existence before the blitz. Sharp recognized this as indicative of the Exeter scene and he sought to perpetuate this effect in the rebuilding of High Street. This aspect of his plan was not approved by the Council, and indeed many of his suggestions or recommendations were not adopted, although some were.

His proposal was for the roadway of High Street to be widened where it was to be rebuilt, so that pedestrians and vehicles alike had more room to move. The upper floors, however, on each side of High Street would be cantilevered over the footpath on each side to retain the intimate 'closeness' of High Street visually.

Sharp also proposed an inner by-pass to the city, but on the north-west side of the centre, running from a proposed roundabout at Blackboy Road to New North Road, via another roundabout near Northernhay and *through* Northernhay Gardens in tunnel. This bypass road would then dip down below Queen Street to connect up with a large clover-leaf flyover junction on the north side of Exe Bridge and outside the old City Wall. Off this bypass road, near the Rougemont Hotel, he had sited his new Bus Station.

In the eventual development, the inner bypass was constructed on the opposite side of the city centre, i.e. to the south-east, where it intercepted the bulk of the traffic before the city centre instead of leaving the traffic to pass through the centre to get to the bypass road at Northernhay.

Sharp also recommended a small roundabout at the South Street junction with Fore Street, and a large rectangular roundabout road system at Eastgate. Neither of these was adopted by the Council, but readers may remember the great debates on the pros and cons of Eastgate Square in the late 1940s and early 1950s. The proposal to construct a roundabout road system at Eastgate, with sunken gardens and subways for pedestrians to cross, was eventually lost by two votes at a special Council meeting on grounds of excessive cost of land. Those readers who have had experience of traffic hold-ups and the problems of pedestrians crossing the road at Eastgate may have their own opinions as to the advantages that might have accrued from the roundabout scheme, besides its striking feature as a focal point and rest garden for shoppers, etc.

Sharp recommended an alternative road parallel to Cowick Street and running to the north of it so that this new road could take the traffic and thus leave the old narrow Cowick Street as a shopping street more suited to the needs of pedestrians. The abandonment of the idea of widening Cowick Street throughout its length in recent years is an indication that the Council have the same ideas now concerning the future of Cowick Street for use as a shopping street. Nevertheless that section of Cowick Street from Exe Bridge to the railway bridge had been widened before that final decision was taken in the early 1960s.

Sharp did, however, make one recommendation that was adopted and constructed and remains to this day, and this was the Pedestrian Shopping Street — since named Princesshay. This was to be a 40 ft wide flagged area whose axial orientation was focused on the north tower of the Cathedral which terminated the vista.

A further recommendation was for a trading estate to be established at Marsh Barton to accommodate not only the bombed-out warehouses and light industries but, in addition, to relocate obsolete and ill-sited factories and the like, and also to attract other industrial firms to Exeter.

It was in this way, by adopting some of the concepts of the plan and rejecting others that the City Council arrived at its approved layout plan for the central area.

THREE
The First Steps

Temporary Shops

The first objective was to try to bring some business back to the devastated areas in the centre of the city, and temporary shops in pre-cast concrete sections were erected at Eastgate.

These were single-storey units flanking the Co-operative Society building (and where the South West Gas Board premises now stand). Further blocks of such buildings were erected on each side of the old road at the top of Southernhay where it emerged on to Eastgate. This old road was later to be obliterated when Eastgate became a simple four-way crossroads and the new widened Paris Street took its place.

These twenty or so shop units formed a very useful, much-needed, attractive shopping area and focal point in an otherwise bleak and barren area of no man's land. Coloured flag-paving was laid in front of these shops and by the old City Wall that still stood in those days. Dwarf walling in red Heavitree stone was constructed with flowers and seats as a small amenity area. This enabled some of the blitzed traders to set up in business and the occupation of one unit by the Post Office – transferring from its emergency site in Queen Street – was an added source of attraction to the shopping public. A similar block of temporary shops was erected on the ruined site of the old Lower Market in Fore Street. These, as at Eastgate, were erected under the responsibility of the City Architect in about 1947–8. They were scheduled to last for ten to fifteen years and enabled the city's trade gradually to expand while the local authority formulated more permanent plans for redeveloping the central area.

1949. Work in Princesshay. Temporary shops in the background

1946. Public Inquiry at the Guildhall (City Council personnel on left; City Planning Officer being questioned by Scott Henderson K.C.)

The Acquisition of Land for Redevelopment

The City Council naturally wished to have control over the architectural aspect of the new building development and to do this it sought powers to acquire large areas of blitzed land and land at the fringes to deal with the area as a whole. Government legislation empowered it to do this.

There was considerable opposition by the traders to this for it meant that many of the traders who had sites of freehold in High Street would have to forfeit their freehold as the Council was permitted by law to acquire and lease the land for development for ninety-nine years.

Little wonder, therefore, that the former High Street traders got together to object to the compulsory purchase powers by the Council and, at a public inquiry held at the Guildhall in 1946, they were represented by such eminent names as Scott-Henderson, McMurtrie and Hugh Park, who were supported by an array of other lawyers and solicitors.

The giving of evidence and the cross-examination between the various barristers representing the traders and Exeter's Town Clerk, Mr C. J. Newman, took several days and, in due course, the Inspector at the inquiry returned to London, considered and later drafted his Report to the Minister. The compulsory acquisition was eventually approved and the way was clear for the Council to prepare the works contract for the Central Areas Reconstruction.

The City Planning Office

Just prior to this public inquiry, the City Council approved the appointment of a new Chief Officer and Department. The City Planning Office thus came into being and those members of the City Engineer's and Surveyor's Department then engaged in this work automatically found themselves no longer under Mr R. H. Dymond, City Engineer. The new Planning Officer was Mr Harold Gayton, one of the City Engineer's senior staff already seconded to assist Mr Sharp in his proposals.

It therefore fell to the lot of Harold Gayton and Thomas Sharp to spend hours in the witness-box, as it were, being cross-examined by Counsel for the traders and the Town Clerk for the Council in the pubic inquiry which was held to declare the area a Redevelopment Area.

In 1947 Mr Dymond retired as City Engineer and Surveyor and he was succeeded in 1948 by Mr John Brierley. A year or so previously – in 1946 – Mr Harold Rowe was appointed City Architect and, for the next twenty-five years, Exeter was to benefit by the vision and purpose of these two men jointly and severally in their respective spheres.

FOUR
Clearance Work

Clearance Work

Work began on the clearance of the area, the removal of old half-walls that were standing and demolition of several of the static water tanks that were sited around the area including the Cathedral Close, Southernhay and Eastgate. Several old basements of shops had also served as water tanks for fire-fighting in emergencies.

Labour was scarce in these immediate post-war years and an approach was made to the Prison Governor to see if prison labour could be used for the demolition of these tanks. And so it was that a gang of convict labour was put to work, watched and supervised the whole time by a warder of the prison.

The Clearance of Burial Grounds

Another aspect of the clearance and preparation of the ground was the need to obtain a faculty for the exhumation and reburial of the graves in some of the city's old churchyards.

The procedure here had to be strictly followed. All legible inscriptions on tombstones were recorded. Some three months' public notice of intention to exhume and reinter elsewhere had to be advertised to give descendants or relations a chance to do any of this work themselves before the local authority stepped in.

The burial ground had to be screened from public view and, in the event of no difficulties being encountered in the procedures, the local authority had to proceed with due reverence to dig and remove gently any remains found and place them in a large wooden container.

A liberal amount of lime had to be available to sprinkle over the ground as necessary and the ground turned over to the requisite depth by hand. The use of machine excavating was not permitted.

The remains were reinterred with reverence in another cemetery and those headstones worth preserving or legible were set in the ground at the place of reinterment.

Such places treated were St Laurence Church in High Street, St George's Church, South Street, Lower Paris Street and, at later dates, Trinity Green, King William Street and, most recently in about 1973, a small area in North Street by St Kerrian's Church (now demolished).

Some of these areas were densely packed with burials, often three layers deep. In St Laurence's churchyard there were 365 burials in 350 square yards, some of which were packed vertically. St Laurence's Church stood approximately 35 yards further down from Castle Street, on the north side of High Street.

1949. Clearance work begins on the site of Deller's Cafe, Bedford Street/Catherine Street corner

FIVE

Co-ordination of Statutory Undertakings' Mains

Co-ordination of Statutory Undertakings' Mains

The first requirement for reconstruction was an accurate large-scale plan of the entire blitzed areas. These areas were surveyed and plotted to a scale of 1 in. to 20 ft so that the thickness of a fine pencil line would represent 2 or 3 in. on that scale. The areas were surveyed with a steel tape and no plotting or drawing was permanently done until the base-lines had been checked as to accuracy of length and direction.

These large-scale plans were to be of enormous value in the plotting of the existing underground services, such as gas, water, telephone cables, electricity cables, and in the locating of new services and manholes, etc.

One of the first jobs to be done in preparing a scheme for redevelopment is to make contact with the various statutory undertakings. By this is meant gas, water, electricity, telephones and, in some cases, Rediffusion, and of course the local authority's Main Drainage Section also comes into this category.

It is most important to know where their pipes or cables are, the position, depth, size and alignment of their existing mains, and also their proposals for new or enlarged mains.

Many meetings took place jointly or severally to determine where, when and how the new mains should be laid. Ideally they are laid beneath the footpaths and the sewers should preferably be in the roadways.

A scheme must be drawn up so that each undertaking has a place to run along the footpath below surface, and it is essential that the *order* of laying is agreed so that they do not get in each other's way. Large-scale plans were drawn with each undertaking's mains located in their final position; and of course existing supplies had to be maintained and allowed for throughout.

Much of this work is done during the early stages of the schemes. It is inevitable that there are what appear to be chaotic scenes of trenches, pits, manholes, etc. However, when the trenches are back-filled, the road pattern begins to take shape and the layman can then see for the first time how the final layout will appear.

Laying G.P.O. 56-way ducts in Musgrave Row, 1951

SIX

The Commemorative Feature in Princesshay

The Commemorative Feature in Princesshay

The Commemorative Feature, near Bedford Street, was constructed in 1949 before any rebuilding in the area had taken place. It was built on the northern tip of the oval green in Bedford Circus.

Tons of Pocombe Stone (that reddish/purple rock with the light-coloured veins traversing it) were delivered to a site nearby between Bedford Circus and Chapel Street. The Council's chief mason, Mr Bill Hutchings, had his little hut erected there and in all weathers for weeks he chipped away at squaring the stone. This was so that construction work, once started, could proceed without interruption.

Care had to be taken over the level of the Feature and the alignment of its longitudinal axis, for at that time no pedestrian shopping street existed and the platform had to conform to the later level of the paving that was to form the street.

The Feature was aligned – as in Sharp's plan – on to the north tower of the Cathedral, and this can be verified on site today with the alignment of the centrally placed lamp columns.

The Feature was designed in the City Architect's Department under Mr

H.R.H. Princess Elizabeth addressing the public at the Commemorative Feature, 21 October 1949

September 1949. Constructing the Commemorative Feature: City Council Direct Labour

Harold Rowe, recently appointed City Architect, and comprised bench-type seats and small flower beds with a central wall plaque in bronze to commemorate the start of the reconstruction of the city.

The Opening Ceremony

Her Royal Highness the Princess Elizabeth (now H.M. The Queen) came to Exeter on 21 October 1949 to set the plaque and name the future pedestrian shopping street 'Princesshay'. ('Hay' is an old word meaning 'fence' or 'hedge' and is a common suffix to many names within the city.) There was, of course, no sign of a street of any kind, just blitzed land. The area around the Feature was, however, fenced with concrete posts and chain-link fencing and gravel was rolled into the ground surrounding the site.

Her Royal Highness walked in procession from the Guildhall, along the blitzed High Street, in company with the Mayor, Major-General (later to become Sir Godwin) Michelmore, the Recorder of the City and the civic dignitaries, all in full regalia, preceded by the Mace Bearers. They turned into Bedford Street, as it then was — lined with cheering crowds — until reaching the Feature where, in company of the Mayor and

Alderman Charles Hill, Chairman of the Planning Committee, Princess performed the Opening Ceremony.

The inscription on the plaque is as follows:

ON THE 21st DAY OF OCTOBER, 1949
THIS TABLET WAS SET HERE BY HER ROYAL HIGHNESS
THE PRINCESS ELIZABETH
DUCHESS OF EDINBURGH
TO MARK THE BEGINNING OF THE REBUILDING
OF THE CITY
LARGELY DESTROYED BY ENEMY AIR RAIDS
IN APRIL — MAY, 1942

Also at the Commemorative Feature were Mr Harold Rowe, Architect, and Mr John Brierley, City Engineer and Surveyor. These chief officers were to make an impact on the redevelopment scene c city for many years to come.

After the setting of the plaque, the Princess later went to lc commemorative stone at Toronto House, Prince Charles Road, whe Home was being built by the City under the Lord Mayor of London' Raid Distress Fund. This is on the present Stoke Hill estate, though a time virtually no development had taken place.

1949. H.R.H. Princess Elizabeth returning from the ceremony at the Commemorative Feature in Princesshay

Financial and Economic Considerations

The acquisition of the High Street area was estimated at the time to be about £2½ million and, before the war, High Street had become one of the highest-valued shopping streets in the country. Frontage values were equivalent to those in Oxford Street, London.

After the initial post-raid 'clearing-up' there was a hiatus in rebuilding until 1948. This was when building licences were made available and thus sites could now be let.

Exeter's first allocation of steel was for 300 tons, and part of this was used for the new Pearl Assurance House which was the first building to be started. Pearl Assurance House is situated in High Street and faces Bedford Street. The next building, started some time later, was the Commercial Union building situated on the same side of High Street but further to the north-east, towards Castle Street.

It will thus be noted that the High Street area was the first part to be redeveloped, Fore Street and Sidwell Street following later as steel allocations, licences and funds permitted. The High Street area of redevelopment comprised about 60 acres.

The letting of sites was the responsibility of the City Estates Surveyor and Valuer, Mr Geoffrey Goss, who worked in close liaison with the Architect and Planning Officer at this time. When sites had been negotiated and agreed, a development company took a block for development rather than one individual shop or office premises. This block would comprise either one large firm or – more usually – a collection of smaller shops or office premises within this block. The speed of redevelopment was partly due to the policy of the City Council in wisely confining its activities to those of a ground landlord and leaving the construction of the buildings to the lessees.

Development took place in an orderly manner, largely through investment companies. By the end of 1953 building on the north side of High Street had virtually been completed. That on the south side was in progress. Negotiations were in hand: in the Fore Street area 90 per cent of the sites were let and in the Sidwell Street area 50 per cent of the sites were let.

Basis for Design

Before building development could take place, however, much road and main drainage work in the High Street area had to be carried out. Furthermore, the City Council had to agree first of all on the future road pattern. This pattern was, of course, tied up with the question of whether the inner bypass road was to be to the north of the central area – as in Sharp's plan – or sited to the south, to intercept traffic before it entered the city centre. After many reports and meetings, estimates and consultations with the Ministry of Transport, police, and so on, the City Council finally decided on the *south* side and plans could then go ahead for Ministry approval on the detailed layout.

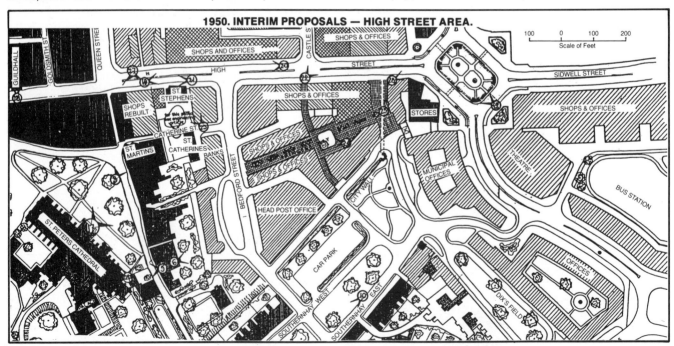

1950. INTERIM PROPOSALS — HIGH STREET AREA.

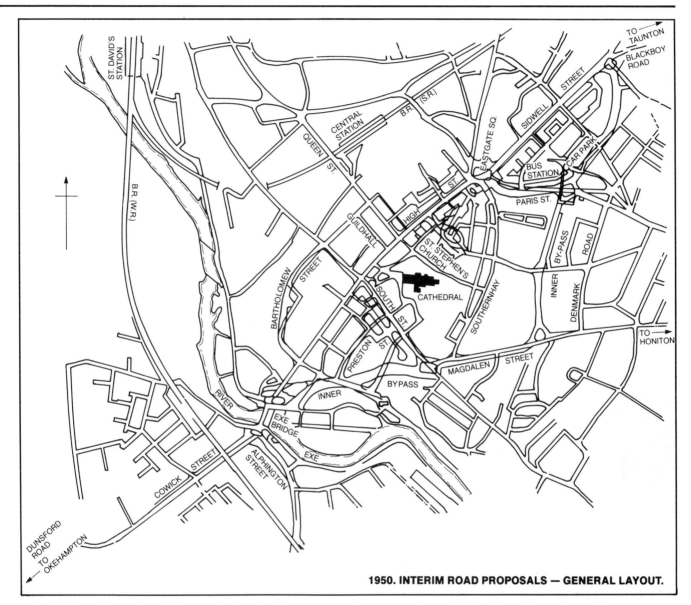

1950. INTERIM ROAD PROPOSALS — GENERAL LAYOUT.

The Ministry of Transport, as it then was, had much influence in the determination of road plans for no work could go ahead without their prior approval. And indeed for main roads such as High Street, Fore Street, South Street and Sidwell Street, the Ministry gave a 75 per cent contribution towards the costs of land acquisition and construction works; but certain clearance items were kept under a separate heading for a separate grant. It therefore followed that, with regard to the government monies then available, those local authorities whose plans were well ahead were more eligible for grants than those authorities who had barely started to formulate their proposals.

Exeter was one of the first local authorities to make a start on reconstruction. This was due to the initiative and drive of the City

Council, officers and staff in getting the preliminary work started and also due, no doubt, to the fact that the new street pattern largely followed the old – streets feeding shopping and business areas that had been established there by earlier generations.

There has come to be, nowadays, some criticism that main streets take buses and general traffic through the middle of shopping areas. This has come to be frowned upon as a danger to the shopping pedestrian, despite the fact that traders like bustle and business at their doors. In 1950 it was the policy of the government to approve main traffic routes through town centres, though one cannot compare the volume of traffic today with the far lesser volume of that time.

1949. Corner improvement at Eastgate nearing completion

EIGHT
The Design of Sewers

The Design of Sewers

A completely new sewerage system was to be laid in the reconstruction areas, for the existing ones were of the old brick-barrel type of construction, damaged in places and often not running in straight lines between manholes. As far as the blitzed areas were concerned, separate sewers were to be laid for storm water and for foul sewers. This was to supersede the old type of combined sewers that existed in these areas.

In the design of foul sewers it had to be remembered that all the shops in the High Street would have basements; it was therefore necessary for the sewers to be laid at such depth that the basements could drain into them, rather than the expensive alternative of pumping basement drainage up to the shallower levels of say an 8 ft depth of sewer below road level. The depths of the foul sewers varied between 18 ft and 24 ft deep to ensure gravitational flow throughout the areas to be drained.

Foul Sewers

The difficulty in designing the size of a sewer at this time was not knowing the type of development or trade that was coming. For instance, a tobacconist's shop uses less water than a restaurant. It was not anticipated then that a laundry or dry-cleaning premises would occupy the High Street. In the event, Paris Street and Fore Street did accommodate such premises and of course the launderettes later to appear in Sidwell Street were not envisaged at that time.

Foul sewers were based on the consumption of water in Exeter at 36 gallons per head per day, given ordinary circumstances. A calculation of the number of people estimated to live or work in each street would indicate the consumption of water, the hours generally used, peak times, etc. From this it was possible to determine the estimated flow from premises between each manhole. Then, depending on the volume of the flow or 'effluent' as it is called, and the gradient of the proposed pipe, one could arrive at the size of pipe required; i.e. whether a 6 in., 9 in., or 12 in. diameter, would suffice, and so on. Starting at the head of the area to be drained (say, Musgrave Row or Bailey Street) fresh inlets would enter the system as the sewers proceeded via Castle Street, High Street, and Bedford Street to the existing sewer in Southernhay West to which they would be connected.

Surface-water Sewers

In the same way, the design of the storm-water sewers (which were not required to accommodate basement flows as was the case in foul sewers) took account of a storm of 1 in. an hour over the area of the road considered, plus that falling on the roof and leading to the sewer, half on to the front of the building and half to the rear. This determined the volume required to be accommodated and the gradient of the proposed sewer between each manhole would determine the size of pipe required. Here again the storm-water system started at Musgrave

Row, took account of any existing flows to be accommodated from outside the system and gradually, according to calculations, the diameter of the pipe would increase with the growing volume of water through the pipes along Bedford Street/Southernhay West, where it connected with the existing sewer.

1950. Foul sewer trench facing Catherine Street
(p. 33) 1950. Surface-water sewer, north side of High Street, facing Eastgate

The Beginning of Reconstruction

A modest start was made in January 1949 by the Council's own Direct Labour Force on tidying up areas and removing such things as old columns and steel stanchions. The force was of course very small at this stage and, as mentioned in Chapter 4, the Prison Governor kindly assisted by drafting in some of the local prisoners in small gangs to carry out unskilled work under supervision.

The First Contract, 1949: Sewers

In July 1949 a contract for £28 000 was started for the laying of foul and surface-water sewers in the High Street area, on the site of future service roads to the north or in the precincts of High Street and Bedford Street.

The foul sewers, being deep, were constructed in tunnel, especially where the depth below the ground exceeded 18 ft. Often these were as much as 24 ft below ground level. Shafts were therefore dug every 120 ft or so where a manhole was to be constructed and an overhead gantry erected with sloping shutes to funnel the excavated material into lorries waiting beneath the gantry. In this way there was the minimum of

May 1950. 15 in. sewer laid in heading
(p. 35) May 1950. Driving heading under High Street to Castle Street

interference to traffic, though the possible dropping of mud on the roads was a factor constantly to be watched.

The tunnels were constructed approximately 4 ft 6 in. high and were supported by stout timber framing every 3 ft along the tunnel. The excavated material was pulled back to the base of shaft in a small truck on rails laid for the purpose. Here it was hoisted to the top of the shute and delivered to the lorries. A maximum 60 ft run was worked from each shaft to avoid ventilation and transportation difficulties.

Each short length of pipe laying was set to grade and level and concreted around. The remainder of the heading was back-filled with 12:1 concrete with large stones (or 'plums') of about 8 in. diameter inserted here and there for added strength.

It will be realized that the tunnelling work of this nature required special skills and stamina, and most of this work was done by imported Irish labour on behalf of the contractor.

The excavated material was used to make up levels for car parking (such as at Leighton Terrace car park), to form embankments for future roads (e.g. the inner by-pass site at Barnfield) or for filling low-lying areas (such as the old clay quarry at Clifton Hill, now an athletic track). These sites were not filled merely from the excavation of trenches and tunnels for the sewers, but also with excavated material from the basement areas of new shop premises as they began to develop. A similar pattern occurred with the excavation in the second contract for roadworks in the High Street area which followed this first contract for sewers.

The City Council, in drawing up building agreements with development companies, stipulated that the Council should decide where excavated material was to be tipped, free of charge. In this way, much of the earthwork of later construction was carried out at little cost to the Council.

It could, perhaps, here be recorded that as the excavation of basements in High Street's new shops gained momentum, the Council was glad to avail itself of the earth filling – one of the sites being at Clifton Hill, as recorded above.

The storm-water sewers followed in the same sequence, but were never more than 12 ft deep, often less though they needed 4 ft of ground cover unless surrounded in concrete. These were laid from the existing sewer connection in Southernhay West via Bedford Street and High Street, Castle Street, Musgrave Row (not yet formed as a street) and Bailey Street (again, not yet formed as a street). Branches were laid to correct line and falls in Catherine Street, Princesshay and what was to be Post Office Street. Pipe diameters varied from 21 in. at the lowest end to 9 in. at the head of the system near Castle Street.

Surface-water sewers were laid in trenches cut for the purpose and the vertical sides were timbered for the safety of the men working. In a few cases the line of the trench crossed bomb craters, roughly filled in after the raid. In order for the new sewers to be on a stable foundation, all debris was excavated and removed until undisturbed ground was found, the cavity then being repacked solid in rubble, consolidated and finished with a 12:1 concrete mix on which the pipes were laid.

The Second Contract, 1950: Roadworks

The High Street area was still the only place where new road and sewer works had been authorized at this time. Fore Street and Sidwell Street areas were to follow later as funds and approvals permitted.

In 1949 a small ceremony took place on the old Bedford Green to mark the beginning of the actual reconstruction work. The centre line of the new Bedford Street was marked out and Alderman W. Slader drove in the vital peg marking the intersection of the centre lines of Princesshay and new Bedford Street. It was an informal affair, the peg being held in position by Mr John Brierley, City Engineer, watched by several members of the Planning Committee and other Council officers. The Planning Committee dealt with reconstruction matters in those days and those present included Aldermen Hill, Wippell, Daw and Tarr, Councillors Harrison, Hunt, Northcott and others. Officials and officers present included Mr Brierley, City Engineer; Mr J. Clitheroe, Deputy City Engineer; Mr H. Gayton, City Planning Officer; Mr G. Goss, City Estate Surveyor; Mr P. France, Engineer in charge of contract; Mr J. Bain, Highways Superintendent.

In September 1950 the second contract (for £40 000) was able to commence. This embodied the construction of the new roads, gulleys and connections to the recently laid sewers; and Post Office telephone cable-laying. In view of the vast amount of new telephone cables to be laid, the Post Office linked their own contract with that of the City so that there would be greater flexibility in operation and simpler control. And so it was that two huts — one for the City's works staff and one for the Post Office engineers' staff — were erected at Bedford Circus and for the next eighteen months or so this was the hub of the reconstruction contract on site.

1950. Ceremony to mark the start of the reconstruction road programme
(The City Engineer carefully holds the peg for an equally careful Alderman Slader)

TEN
Work on Various Streets

Bedford Street

In order to minimize inconvenience to traffic, it was essential to provide a new Bedford Street before dispensing with the old; a start was therefore made on the excavation, preparation and consolidation of the area to be paved as roadway, as one of the first objectives. The line of the new street lay parallel to the old Bedford Street and traversed the ruined ground floor of Lloyds Bank on the High Street/Bedford Street corner and also the former well-known Deller's Cafe on the Bedford Street/Catherine Street corner. The breaking up of the floor of Lloyds Bank was very heavy work, particularly where the former strong room was situated.

The sewer had previously been laid through these premises and was several feet below the basement. The floor was of reinforced concrete and debris had filled the various basement ruins. The confined spaces and the necessary removal of old shelving and fittings added considerably to the difficulties in clearing the premises.

It is no good constructing a road on foundations of charred and rotted timber, glass, paper ashes, slates and open voids, which was indeed what was encountered in many old basements and in bomb craters quickly back-filled after the raids. A very large deep crater was found at Catherine Street and excavation had to go down to 15 ft or more to arrive at firm ground. The huge cavity had to be back-filled with hand-packed

The completed Bedford Street, looking towards Southernhay, 1954

1950. The new Bedford Street takes shape alongside the old (The Commemorative Feature is just visible inside the Green of Bedford Circus)

May 1950. Pit for manhole formed in hand-packed filling in old bomb crater, Bedford Street

bricks, the crevices filled and rammed solid with gravel and stone in layers for the full depth of the hole. Indeed, this was the case where old basements existed too, as in High Street when this came to be widened in 1961, for the wider roadway naturally embraced land formerly occupied by buildings.

It is not surprising that, on Deller's site, the odd spoon or piece of cutlery, bent, corroded or tarnished, was uncovered in the course of the work. And occasionally molten coins in a cash-box — caused by the intense heat of the blitz — were also found.

Catherine Street

A design was prepared and a contract let for underground conveniences to be built at Catherine Street in the area near St Stephen's Church. These conveniences were to replace those that existed in Bedford Street which were later to be demolished. The gentlemen's in Bedford Street was situated below ground but longitudinally in the centre of the road. The ladies' was also below ground but adjacent to the Green in Bedford Street and indeed was in close proximity to the Commemorative Feature, opened by Princess Elizabeth in 1949.

In Catherine Street the ruins of St Katherine's Almshouses exist to this day and have been perpetuated as a memorial to the destruction with the laying of turf and seats as a quiet resting place for the public and holiday-makers in particular.

The completion and final opening of the new underground conveniences in Catherine Street had to be delayed for some time to allow the completion of the new Catherine Street roadway itself.

St Katherine's Almshouses before being cleared and set out as a memorial, 1956

The Low-level Service Road

This road had to be excavated down to basement level to serve the basements of the premises now beginning to be built in Princesshay (north side) and High Street (south side). Masses of earth were excavated and the sides left at a 45° slope until construction of the shops took place. The excavated material – as with most of the material being excavated by other contractors for the shops – was transported to Barnfield at Fairpark for an embankment to take, in later years, the inner by-pass. Thousands of cubic yards were dumped here annually.

The excavation for the low-level service road, as was expected, severed a length of the famous underground passages, exposing in the deep cutting the aperture with its masonry surround. Regrettably, before the exposed opening could be bricked up, someone entered the passage from this end and stole a quantity of lead forming the conduit half buried in the floor. It is understood that, within a matter of days, the culprit was caught and brought to justice, though of course the conduit replacement was lost for all time.

The huge excavated area was left with sloping banks and fenced around for safety until development companies were able to complete negotiations and arrange for contracts to be let for erecting buildings at the Bedford Street end of Princesshay. At this time, therefore, the Commemorative Feature stood alone and its alignment and central position in what was to be a pedestrian shopping street were as yet not appreciated by the public.

Meanwhile, a block of shops with office accommodation overhead was nearing completion at the top end of Princesshay and it was always the Council's practice to lay paving up to the threshold of any shop before its opening date. Thus an area of flagged paving 8 ft wide was laid correct to final levels and falls outside this first section of Princesshay to be completed.

Post Office Street

This road, as in the case of Princesshay, was constructed as a completely new street. It was named Post Office Street only when the site for the Head Post Office was finally agreed at a later date and work of constructing it was well under way.

The road ran parallel to the old City Wall on the opposite side from Southernhay, which had yet to be laid out as a large surface car park. It crossed the site of the old Bluecoat School, the raised concrete platform of which still stood near the gap in the wall. This platform had to be demolished of course, but by the time this work was carried out, weeds and Buddleia shrubs were growing here and there on the levelled sites adjoining. Nature was doing her best to hide the scars of man's wanton damage of ten years before.

It will be observed that the existence of the Bluecoat School has been commemorated in Princesshay with the diminutive statue of a small boy in one of the central garden beds.

Before construction of the roadway, squatters had moved into an old

The north-east end of Post Office Street under construction, 1952: part of the City Wall can be seen on the right

lean-to hut by the City Wall; they had to be moved out before work could start.

Work was by this time taking shape on the building of shops and showrooms on the south side of Princesshay. Every developer, before commencing work, had to find out the position, size, depth, gradient and type (storm-water or foul) of the nearest sewers to the site. He would also need to know the relative positions of gas, water, electricity, telephone cables, existing or proposed services. And before digging the foundations, he would also need to know the final level of the paving that would abut the site and the City Council staff would check the line, frontage and depth of the site as marked out by the developer's representative on the site. A steel tape-measure was always used and measurements were to the nearest ⅛ in.

At the northern end of the City Wall, by Post Office Street, the old bastion had been damaged but a length of wall between the bastion and Eastgate that fronted the temporary shops remained standing at this time as the temporary shops were of course in use and had become very popular. The wall at this point was later to be demolished, when the shops had served for about fifteen years, to make way for Eastgate House, the South West Gas Board and other offices as we now know them. The line of this length of the City Wall has been marked in the flagged paving by a crazy-paving strip and a bronze tablet was let into the ground at Eastgate years later.

Post Office Street itself at this time – about 1952 – stopped short half-way round the bend at the Bastion; and the Bastion was completed in stone in keeping with the rest of the City Wall.

The stone found in the above-ground sections of the City Wall comprises stone no longer quarried:

Pocombe stone – as in the Princesshay Feature – is a hard, purplish stone with white veins traversing it.

Heavitree stone is a red sandstone, red as the soil of Devon. It has to be laid on its bedding face or the exposed flank would weather away.

Thorverton stone is a deeper-purple-coloured stone with pock marks, reminiscent of a sponge in appearance.

Bailey Street and Castle Street

The shops on the north side of High Street were nearing completion and it was now possible for the road contractors to carry out their work. This needed much co-ordination and co-operation for the new shops had their own haulage, deliveries, work-forces and hutted accommodation.

The Pearl Assurance block had been the first off the mark, quickly followed by the Commercial Union. Third was Marks & Spencer who built on a series of piled foundations in grid formation. Marks & Spencer's contractors confined their activities solely to the site within their boundaries. Hutments, stores of reinforcement bars, bricks, etc. were all brought to site the very moment they were required. It was a

Bailey Street: underpinning the wall, 1951

most orderly operation throughout and a masterpiece of organization.

In Castle Street the Post Office Engineers laid a multiple fifty-six-way duct diagonally across the new road (now widened to 48 ft overall); it had to be laid at sufficient depth to clear the other mains and services in the street. The number of these cables had increased owing to the greater proximity of the telephone exchange, and plans were afoot to extend this building further west towards the Gandy Street direction.

In Bailey Street the high wall bounding the British Legion Hall had to be underpinned and built with mass concrete in short lengths because the roadway was constructed at a lower level than the original wall. The whole was faced up in Heavitree stone in keeping with the surroundings.

At the rear of Marks & Spencer's site there was a bottleneck in the new road (Bailey Street) until a few buildings in Castle Street were demolished. Huge shores were erected to support the end of the block. These shores are there to this day and enabled Bailey Street to link up with Castle Street at its normal width. The only difficulty was that the level of the new service road meant a very steep connection with Little Castle Street, despite an attempt to minimize this steepness by raising Bailey Street at the Castle Street end. In Castle Street the new Westminster Bank, as it was then, was reconstructed on its own site on the High Street corner while business went on.

*Junction of Castle Street with High Street, 1951
(Ruined Westminster Bank on the right)*

Musgrave Row

Musgrave Row, with the small car-park area adjoining, was constructed at this time (about 1952), though the breakthrough to connect to Gandy Street took place at a later date. It then linked up with Little Queen Street which, in turn and later still, was widened to give a standard 20 ft carriageway through to Queen Street. The car-parking area was extended by one third of its size at a later date when the new City Library was built in 1965. The high retaining wall, steps and ramped path were, however, constructed at the time that Musgrave Row was first made.

Musgrave Row naturally gets its name from Musgrave Alley. Bailey Street was so named from the association with the Castle and the Keep.

In trenching for the sewers in Musgrave Row, the curve of the old Castle moat was evident in the exposed trench face, due to the change in appearance of the soil. Archaeologists at the University at that time were notified and records taken before back-filling.

High Street had not yet been widened, though the new shops were set back to allow for this work in the future (about 1961 – 62). Footpaths were temporarily paved to the new shops as they opened, giving very wide areas on each side of the still comparatively narrow carriageway of the old High Street.

An arcade was being formed opposite Castle Street to link up with Princesshay and further on to Post Office Street, this arcade being 'bridged' over the low-level service road referred to earlier.

It is not intended to go into detail, street by street, of the method of construction. Much of it was repetitive and involved frequent meetings with developers, statutory undertakings, police, transport departments, etc. A chronological list of works will be found later in this narrative to indicate the intensity of planning, design and construction that went into the rebuilding of the city centre during this period.

ELEVEN
Princesshay

Princesshay

The construction of Princesshay was spread over a period of twelve years or so. From the building of the Commemorative Feature in 1949 there was a pause until the completion of Singers' corner block at the top end, when a strip of flagging was laid for part of the width of Princesshay for the use of shoppers. As building developed in the later years, so would the flagged paving be extended.

The work was carried out by the Council's direct labour force as and when necessary and – as with all new sites – the future finished paving levels were provided to the building developers at an early stage. Princesshay is nominally 40 ft wide with a 6 in. cross-fall to a central channel where gulleys pick up surface water and convey it to the sewer.

The foul and surface-water sewers were laid in Princesshay after the Feature was built and there was evidence of some slight subsidence resulting from the weakening of the ground. As a precaution, therefore, the flank of the Feature's raft foundation was strutted at intervals with three steel joists which sloped into the ground and were bedded in concrete for taking any thrust.

The flagging in Princesshay was laid in grid formation and the longitudinal joists were set out by theodolite to obviate a possible 'wavey' appearance when viewed from either end. The flagstones were specially made of reconstructed York Stone and were made – as with all other flags used by the City – 2½ in. thick.

Exeter was one of the very few local authorities to retain the use of 2½ in. flags, as opposed to 2 in. or even 1½ in. for decorative work. Anyone who has handled even 1½ in. flagstones will know the weight

1952. A start has been made on Princesshay

involved in manoeuvring them; how much greater the 2½ in. thickness.

Princesshay was to be restricted to pedestrian traffic, although special dispensation was given to the Post Office for mail delivery, when pneumatic tyres are used on an electrically operated vehicle.

Lamp columns were centrally placed and lined up with the north tower of the Cathedral as the orientation follows Sharp's proposal. Garden-beds and seats were provided for amenity and in 1960 a new entrance to the Underground Passages was constructed and embodied in a flower-bed with seating accommodation.

Princesshay was finally completed in 1962 when buildings on both sides had been established.

Princesshay, being constructed on land that was hitherto not a public highway, had not at first the same public protection that was applicable to highways. The Council controlled it as ground landlords.

Problems occurred when it was found that public disturbances could not directly be dealt with by the police without express request by the Council. For instance, on the odd occasion of turbulent political meetings, college rags or other incidents, where perhaps paint was daubed or unruly behaviour occurred, it meant that a representative of the Council had to be on hand to call for police assistance. Subsequently, however, the City Council passed a resolution declaring the street to be a public highway so that any necessary police measures would be automatic and not dependent on a request of the ground landlord.

March 1957. Work on Princesshay progresses
(Temporary shops still visible at side of Co-operative Society building)

(p. 43) March 1957. Princesshay, looking towards Bedford Street

TWELVE
The City Wall

The City Wall

One effect of the bombing of the city was that it opened up to view sections of the old City Wall hitherto hidden or screened by former building development. Exeter was fortunate in that the length of the City Wall had been preserved for almost the whole of its perimeter. The wall became more visible at Paul Street, Bartholomew Street West, The Friars and Trinity Street, where outworn buildings had been demolished; and at Southernhay West and Eastgate as a result of the bombing.

There were of course gaps in the wall and some damaged bastions. In Southernhay West, too, a building or two and a hideous electricity sub-station had been constructed abutting the wall which marred the continuity of walling. In the post-war development, however, more gaps were to be made by the formation of a roadway junction at Southernhay West and a much larger gap at The Friars where the later inner bypass cut through the wall. A further length between Eastgate and Southernhay West was removed to permit the construction of the top end of Princesshay, though here, as mentioned earlier, the line of the wall has been permanently indicated by a length of crazy paving.

Such ancient monuments as the City Wall could not be demolished without the authority of the then Ministry of Works who had first to be satisfied that the end justified the means. The ministry laid down regulations for recording the ancient monument before it was lost for ever. This involved measuring, surveying and plotting, photographing and a written report.

The bastions at the top of Southernhay and at Trinity Street were repaired in a manner in keeping with the medieval walling using Pocombe stone (veined) or Thorverton stone (pitted); but, regrettably, the present-day buttresses at the opening in the wall opposite the Head Post Office have left the stamp of the twentieth century on this severance, particularly on the northern section face – a very disappointing treatment. The severance at the Friars has been faced up in a different style again, but still at variance with the original medieval pattern.

It is understood that the Roman section of the wall at Southernhay is just below ground level, the walling above being mostly medieval. In the more recent development at Broadwalk House it is observed that the soil and planting has now buried by a few feet in depth what has been stated to be Roman walling.

An archway in the City Wall, now demolished, facing Southernhay (Ruin of Southernhay Congregational Church is visible through the archway)

1965. View of Southernhay car parks, City Wall and Post Office Street

Southernhay

Following the formation of the two surface car parks in Southernhay West in 1952, work then switched to the lower end where, at Trinity Green, the burial ground was carefully and laboriously cleared. Trinity Green was formerly enclosed by a masonry wall 4 ft high and many tombstones were erected backing onto this boundary wall. Others were of course in the green itself. Many were illegible through erosion over the years; some were tilted due to ground settlement. It was said that the burials — being just outside the old City Wall — were victims of the plague whose bodies were disposed of at the nearest point outside the walls.

In accordance with the Regulations, however, all inscriptions that were legible were recorded and located. After due public notice, the Council's workmen, under Mr Reg Green, erected a screened enclosure and proceeded with the authorized exhumation. From time to time, when the ground within the enclosure was cleared, the screening was moved to a different part of the green and the process continued. Reburials took place on consecrated ground at Higher Cemetery, Hamlin Lane.

The greens in Southernhay were formerly the responsibility of the respective frontagers and they were maintained or neglected to varying degrees. The greens were all grass-covered but were enclosed by a rough privet hedge about 3 ft high which acted as a deterrent to the public and kept these open spaces private. No flower-beds existed and the overall appearance was rather drab. The granite coping at the edges bore evidence of the surrender of iron railings for the war effort.

Negotiations with the frontagers resulted in all four greens in

June 1952. Southernhay car parks under construction (Note temporary shops in background)

May 1952. Southernhay West before construction of car parks (Note old substation and City Wall on left)

1952. Dwarf walling and flower beds around top car park

Southernhay being made available for public use. The City Council already controlled the first or lowest green because the Municipal Offices, Nos 2–10, occupied the terrace opposite to it.

It was at the time that the car parks were being completed that a transformation took place, creating Southernhay as we know it today. Credit for this must go to the City Engineer, Mr Brierley, who recommended the removal of the privet hedges and substitution of flower borders in beds of varying width throughout the length of the greens. Old shrubs were cut out and trees preserved, with the judicious planting of others. Seats were also provided for the benefit of the public. The seasonal blaze of floral colour was provided from the newly established Propagation Centre and Nurseries at Belle Isle. Dwarf walling in Heavitree stone enclosed the car parks with a colourful display of flowers and shrubs which helped partly to screen the cars from public view.

At Trinity Green the cleared ground was now able to be converted to a car park, which was also screened by dwarf walling and shrubs. A shelter and conveniences were built opposite the old Royal Devon and Exeter Hospital and these were to prove of great benefit to visitors and others waiting outside the hospital which was then established in Southernhay.

Traffic signals that operated at the junction of Barnfield Road and Southernhay East were dispensed with for, in 1954 one-way traffic was introduced in Southernhay East and West. This greatly eased traffic congestion; with vehicles parked at the kerbside (and particularly outside the old Municipal Offices), two-way traffic in Southernhay East and West had caused considerable problems.

The beautifying of Southernhay led the way to the brightening up of many odd corners of the city by the use of grassed areas, flowerbeds, dwarf walling and isolated trees in paving.

1952. Southernhay West, lower car park constructed

FOURTEEN

Eastgate

Eastgate

During the early fifties the City Council was much concerned with Eastgate and how this intersection should be treated in its ultimate layout. Thomas Sharp, in his proposals, had made provision for a 'Square' to be formed by new buildings which embraced the intersection of the four main entering roads – New North Road, Sidwell Street, Paris Street and High Street. Sharp had, within the square, formed a roundabout for the converging roads in the form of an oblong design with the long axis parallel to High Street and Sidwell Street.

Mr Brierley and Mr Rowe (the City Engineer and City Architect respectively) had between them jointly designed a square, but with the rectangular road roundabout set diagonally to the four entering roads to facilitate traffic flow whilst at the same time retaining the 'enclosing' effect of the fronting buildings of the square.

The 'Sunken Garden' Scheme for Eastgate

It was at once realized that this would be a very important focal point, not only for vehicular traffic but also for pedestrians, and the modified design therefore took account of these opposing interests.

The design allowed for a sunken garden in the centre of the roundabout where pedestrians could rest on seats set amid flower gardens and to which access was obtained via pedestrian subways beneath the roundabout carriageways. There were to be four subways – one on each side of the roundabout – and each one would be linked to a pedestrian ramp in the pavement situated behind the kerb and sloping up to pavement level at a gradient of 1 in 10. All electricity and telephone cables were to be taken to the island and concealed beneath a peripheral 'mound'.

Because High Street, Sidwell Street and Paris Street were first-class roads the then Ministry of Transport was responsible for 75 per cent of the capital cost of the Eastgate Scheme. The Ministry was in favour of a traffic-signal-control scheme which was the least costly of any scheme, but in no way could it solve the pedestrian problems. The Ministry was opposed to the City Council's roundabout scheme which provided for the segregation of pedestrians. Many plans, reports, statistics, deputations and arguments between the City Council and the Ministry extended over a period of eight years. In the end the Ministry stated that it could not find anything technically wrong with the Council's scheme, and was prepared to give approval provided that the City Council would accept a grant of 75 per cent of the capital cost of the traffic-signal scheme, which was much less than the capital cost of the roundabout scheme. The City Council rejected this offer by a majority of two votes.

The Crossroads Scheme at Eastgate

The alternative of having a simple crossroads with traffic signals was therefore adopted for this vital intersection. Observers will notice that the gaps in the central reservation are wider than was hitherto customary in order to accommodate the large crowds that would need to wait there to cross the road.

Motorists and pedestrians alike may pause and reflect, as they now wait to turn right from Paris Street into Sidwell Street, how much

The original plan for Eastgate Square

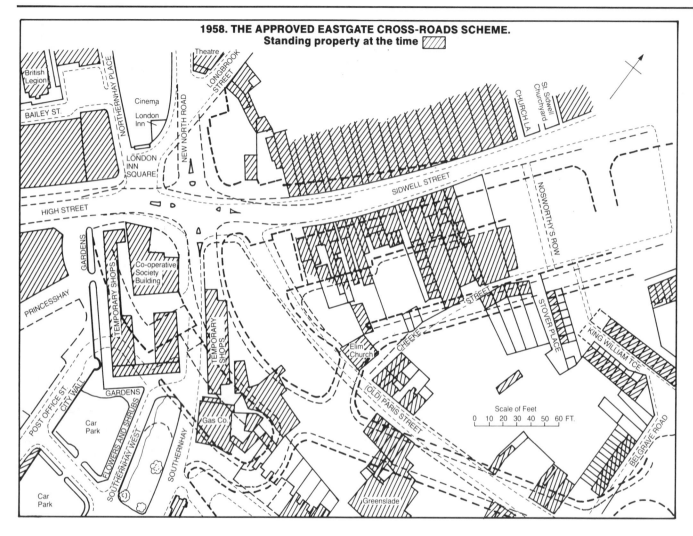

1958. THE APPROVED EASTGATE CROSS-ROADS SCHEME.
Standing property at the time

British Legion

BAILEY ST.

NORTHERNHAY PLACE

Cinema
London Inn

LONDON INN SQUARE

NEW NORTH ROAD

Theatre

LONGBROOK STREET

CHURCH LA.

St. Sidwell Churchyard

SIDWELL STREET

NOSWORTHY'S ROW

HIGH STREET

GARDENS

Co-operative Society Building

PRINCESSHAY

TEMPORARY SHOPS

TEMPORARY SHOPS

Elim Church

CHEEKE STREET

STOVER PLACE

KING WILLIAM TCE

POST OFFICE ST.
CITY WALL

GARDENS

Car Park

Gas Co

FLOWERS AND SHRUBS

SOUTHERNHAY WEST

SOUTHERNHAY

(OLD) PARIS STREET

Scale of Feet
0 10 20 30 40 50 60 FT.

BELGRAVE ROAD

Car Park

Greenslade

smoother would have been the flow of traffic around the roundabout had that scheme been adopted. It should of course be pointed out that with the more recent prohibition of vehicles in High Street and the one-way traffic in Sidwell Street, the traffic problem today is not as acute as it used to be.

The author built a scale model of Eastgate in 1958 as it was proposed on the crossroads principle, and in the ensuing years the actual scheme was completed at Eastgate in 1960. The widening of High Street followed a year later, to be completed in 1962.

The new Paris Street was realigned at Eastgate to emerge opposite to New North Road. The build-up of the road level to form superelevation along its sharp curve – and its reduction to normal camber at the approach to Eastgate – makes a very comfortable ride.

It is worth recording here that at the time of publication a proposal has been submitted for the redevelopment of the bus station and Debenhams sites. This would put Paris Street back on its earlier alignment, but in a tunnel under Sidwell Street, enabling the creation of a pedestrianized London Inn Square!

1958. Venning's model of Eastgate crossroads scheme

FIFTEEN

High Street

HIGH ST. AREA — NEW ROAD LAYOUT — 1976.

Existing property

City Wall

New development

(1) Commemorative Feature
(2) Catherine Street underground conveniences
(3) City Library Extension
(4) Telephone Exchange Extension
(5) Eastgate House
(6) Entrance to underground passages
(7) Broadwalk House (on site of former surface car park)
(8) Head Post Office
(9) Civic Centre

High Street

The Post Office authorities had allowed in the contract for huge underground chambers to be constructed at the Eastgate and Queen Street junctions. The size of cable was approximately 4 in. diameter and, in order to turn a right-angle, a chamber measuring about 12 ft × 8 ft was required in the carriageway and had to be many feet deep to clear other services and mains.

carriageways and a central reservation of 4 ft.

To carry out this work required the co-operation of all. Meetings were held with the Chamber of Trade, Transport Department, police and motoring organizations, and each individual firm affected in High Street was notified in advance.

All vehicular traffic, including buses, was diverted while the work was in progress and the operation appeared to proceed without serious trouble, though of course the traders were anxious for normal conditions to return. The work started in 1960/61 and was completed the following year. It followed the completion of the Eastgate crossroads improvement.

The Post Office authorities had allowed in the contract for huge underground chambers to be constructed at the Eastgate and Queen Street junctions. The size of cable was approximately 4 in, diameter and, in order to turn a right-angle, a chamber measuring about 12 ft × 8 ft was required in the carriageway and had to be many feet deep to clear other services and mains.

The concrete carriageway of the old High Street had, of course, to be broken out and I well remember the frantic reaction of the Gas Company when the contractors brought in a 20-ton thumper which proceeded to drop its weight on the concrete to break it like a slab of chocolate! Needless to say, this method had only limited use, because the gas mains, if too shallow, would fracture.

1952. Site between Catherine Street and High Street (formerly Lloyds Bank and part of Deller's Cafe)

SIXTEEN
Fore Street/South Street Area

Condition in 1945

The area of devastation was smaller here than in High Street but both Fore Street and South Street were shopping streets and this, together with the destruction of the lower market building, represented a great loss to the community and the residential area nearby.

On the north side of Fore Street from Cornish's/Brocks to St Olave's Church, the land was laid waste, as was the land from South Street to Market Street on the south side of Fore Street. In South Street itself, from High Street down to Bear Street, the old buildings had been levelled to the ground. A gaping hole at the top end had opened up the view of the west front of the Cathedral and also of the Church of St Mary Major which partially masked it. (The church was later demolished for redevelopment of the Cathedral approach in the early 1970s.)

The ruin of the old Hall of the Vicars Choral abutting Kalendarhay was preserved as a ruin and a plaque may be seen within its walls. Also in South Street on the Cathedral side – but between Palace Gate and Holy Trinity Church – the land was substantially levelled for redevelopment later.

The area bounded by Fore Street and South Street and extending to Coombe Street was a cleared area and was made available for the parking of vehicles, free for all, to keep the roads clear.

There was a small burial ground near the top of South Street on the site of a church known as St George's Church. This of course had to be properly cleared and reburials made before development could take place, as in the case of St Laurence's Church, High Street, and Trinity Green in Southernhay.

At the Coombe Street end of the area there were old tenement blocks with railed balconies overlooking Coombe Street. These were known as Cotton's Buildings, Coffins Place, and so on, and formed part of a densely populated residential area, most of which has since been demolished to make way for commercial development.

The Old Road Pattern

Two streets and half of another street cut across the blitzed site from South Street and have since disappeared. Near the top of South Street a very narrow street, George Street, connected South Street to the flank of the old Lower Market where an old monument and convenience were situated. Further down was Guinea Street, half the length of which still remains at the rear of the rebuilt market. The other road was Sun Street, in line with Preston Street but, like part of Guinea Street and George Street, it was closed under statutory proceedings to enable development to take place. The lower end of Market Street may be said to approximate to the old Sun Street, emerging as it does on to the lower section of South Street between Bear Street and Palace Gate, but on the opposite side.

It should be remembered that – like High Street – Fore Street and South Street were only about half the width of the present streets, and the old granite kerbs were chipped and broken through age and as a result of war damage. George Street has, in name, been perpetuated by the

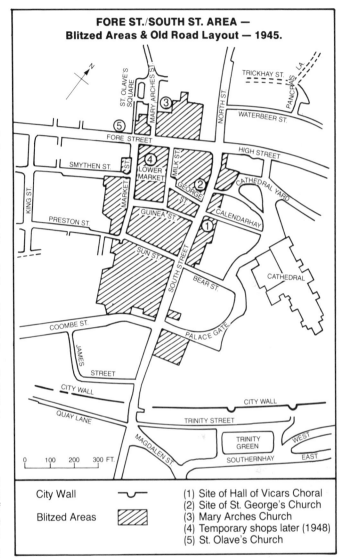

**FORE ST./SOUTH ST. AREA —
Blitzed Areas & Old Road Layout — 1945.**

| City Wall | ⌐ |
| Blitzed Areas | ▨ |

(1) Site of Hall of Vicars Choral
(2) Site of St. George's Church
(3) Mary Arches Church
(4) Temporary shops later (1948)
(5) St. Olave's Church

service road constructed in the 1950s behind the shops in South Street.

The old Milk Street, running along the north flank of the Lower Market, was virtually a narrow lane with little or no footpaths. The only vestige of this that remains is the adapted arcade on the Fore Street frontage.

On the north side of old Fore Street the narrow Mary Arches Street linked with Bartholomew Street. There was a delightful old group of buildings forming a small enclosure, known as St Olave's Square, and situated approximately opposite St Mary Arches Church. This area, derelict as it was, gave way to redevelopment in the widening of Mary Arches Street in the mid 1950s and a short cul-de-sac opposite the church in Mary Arches Street was later added in the 1960s. The derelict land on the north side of Mary Arches Street at the rear of the then Gaumont Cinema (now a Bingo Hall) was converted for surface car parking, being one of the earliest sites to be specially prepared for the purpose. It was, and still can be, approached by pedestrians from North Street by means of ancient covered passageways, the most noted being Chapple's Court.

Redevelopment

By 1952/53, the second roads contract for High Street area had been completed and the shops on the north side of High Street had been built; the shops on the south side were in progress and the first block of shops at the top end of Princesshay (Singers, etc.) was completed.

Two surface car parks at Southernhay West were completed, the filling for the low-lying gardens and basements being supplied free from the excavations in the High Street area.

Sites had by this time been let, and building commenced in South Street and at the corner of Fore Street; development gradually spread downhill over the ensuing years.

In the Fore Street/South Street area certain procedures had first to be

November 1953. Construction of service road behind South Street (Now known as George Street; ruins of old market on left)

followed before work could start. A burial ground had to be cleared at George Street. Then George Street had to be legally 'closed' so that building could take place on the site of the highway. This also applied to half of Guinea Street and to Sun Street, which was obliterated altogether.

The ruin of the Hall of the Vicars Choral at the junction of Kalendarhay and South Street was to be retained as a memorial; it is still there today.

Milk Street, alongside the north flank of the lower market, was all but swallowed up by the proposed turning space to the service road that served the backs of South Street and Fore Street. The City Architect's Department had designed shops and maisonettes between this service road and South Street and these were built after the service road had been constructed. The service road was later to be named George Street and was the first construction in this area, together with the widening of Mary Arches Street (from Fore Street to the church). These two minor roads preceded work on the widening of South Street and Fore Street until construction of the buildings had become sufficiently advanced for these latter roads to be widened a few years later.

South Street service road (now George Street) was constructed through levelled waste ground and was for some time a bus route, with a terminus at the top end, while building went on in the main street. Mary Arches Street surface car park was constructed at this time, and

1953. Construction of shops in South Street before widening (Old Sun Street built over; new service road (George Street) being used as temporary bus route and terminus)

development was taking place in Fore Street frontage.

The Fore Street buildings were set back — as in High Street — to give 74 ft between opposite sides of the road. This allowed for two 15 ft footways and a carriageway of 44 ft. The 44 ft was made up of two lanes of 20 ft in each direction with a central island refuge 4 ft wide.

At Market Street, where the City Architect had plans for a new lower market and hall, the proposal was to widen Fore Street on the south side; indeed the kerb was laid to allow for this and is still visible on site.

July 1955. South Street (Stage 1): widening in progress

In fact, however, the proposal to prescribe a widening line down Fore Street was abandoned years later and so the widening tapered back to the old width at Market Street.

South Street itself was constructed in two stages: Stage I — from Fore Street to Coombe Street (in 1955/56); Stage II — from Coombe Street to Magdalen Street (in 1957/58). The road is nominally of 30 ft carriageway with two 15 ft footpaths where the new shops have been erected. The carriageway widens out to 40 ft with a 4 ft central island at its junction with Fore Street, where traffic signals were renewed.

South Street has an excellent riding quality and the lack of jolting is apparent as one rides up the hill at moderate speed.

Later Market Street was completed to link up with South Street, and the new market on the site of the old lower market was designed and constructed by the Council, with St George's Hall and the shops fronting Fore Street forming a unified architectural group.

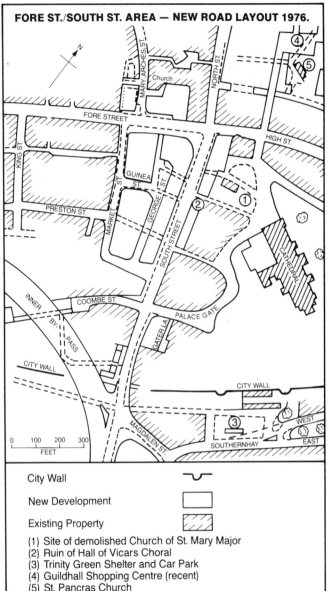

FORE ST./SOUTH ST. AREA — NEW ROAD LAYOUT 1976.

City Wall		⌄⌄
New Development		▢
Existing Property		▨

(1) Site of demolished Church of St. Mary Major
(2) Ruin of Hall of Vicars Choral
(3) Trinity Green Shelter and Car Park
(4) Guildhall Shopping Centre (recent)
(5) St. Pancras Church

SEVENTEEN

Sidwell Street Area

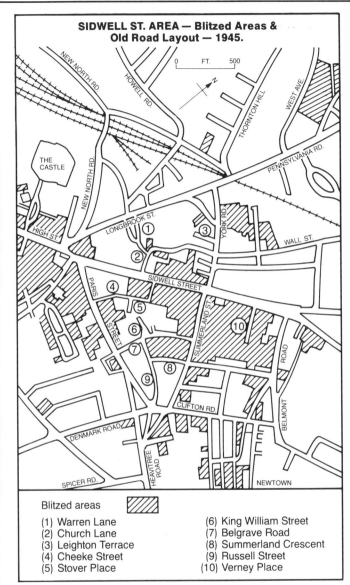

SIDWELL ST. AREA — Blitzed Areas & Old Road Layout — 1945.

Blitzed areas

(1) Warren Lane
(2) Church Lane
(3) Leighton Terrace
(4) Cheeke Street
(5) Stover Place
(6) King William Street
(7) Belgrave Road
(8) Summerland Crescent
(9) Russell Street
(10) Verney Place

Condition in 1945

This was the largest area of devastation, though it contained more isolated buildings that had either escaped destruction or had been patched up to continue functioning.

The lofty terrace comprising small shops with living accommodation above, running north-east from Summerland Street and opposite Sidwell Street Methodist Church, escaped destruction and is still standing today. On the site of the present Devon General garage in Belgrave Road stood the Co-operative Society's Dairy and Stores and garages.

On the north side of Sidwell Street the land was derelict from St Sidwell's Church and burial ground to York Road. On the south side, from a point approximately where Homesense now stands to the junction of Blackboy Road/Belmont Road (excepting the terrace referred to above), the land was virtually levelled to the ground. This was also the case from Acland Road (Acland Terrace as it then was) to Clifton Road (still evidenced by the pathway running across the car park at The Triangle and in line with Clifton Road).

The remainder of Sidwell Street — i.e. from St Sidwell's churchyard to what is now Eastgate — remained standing, as shops with offices or living accommodation above. At that time these were built up to within a few feet of the old kerb line, but all this frontage has now been set back and rebuilt to a line which was to allow for a dual carriageway, though this has never materialized.

The Old Road Pattern

Sidwell Street was much wider than High Street, Fore Street or South Street, particularly at its north-eastern end where, even today, no change in the carriageway width has taken place.

Its central section between Summerland Street and St Sidwell's Church has varied but little; the old kerb is still in its original position on the south side. A slight variation on the north side is evident by the traffic signals at York Road.

On the north side of Sidwell Street were several courts or alleyways passing beneath arches in the buildings fronting the main street, similar to those in High Street. These included Jones' Court, Wesleyan Place, Passmore's Court and Chanter's Court.

Those on the south side included Baker's Court, Gatty's Court, Gill's Court, Shepherd's Court, Adelaide Court, Strong's Cottages, Townsend's Court, Southard's Court, Red Lion Court and others. Nosworthy's Row was at the boundary of the blitzed area opposite St Sidwell's churchyard. Sherrell's Court survived for several more years and is approximately at the boundary between the old terrace of shops opposite York Road and the later maisonettes built opposite the Odeon cinema.

Within the Sidwell Street/Paris Street quarter were a number of roads completely devoid of premises, such as Summerland Crescent and Russell Street; others were fronted by old cottages, ripe for demolition and/or redevelopment and whose names have been perpetuated elsewhere. These were King William Terrace, Stover Place, Belgrave

Road, Cheeke Street, Verney Place, etc. The general area comprised mixed development with small blocks of cottages interspersed with light-industrial premises. The old Paris Street skirted along its southern flank and the land between Paris Street and Dix's Field was generally devastated also.

Paris Street, as with South Street, Fore Street and High Street, had carriageways of approximately 22 ft or 24 ft in places. Sidwell Street, however, was nearer to 40 ft. It should be borne in mind that the widths of these streets were only about half what they are today.

Statutory Road Closures

Before any redevelopment could proceed on any site that was affected by an existing highway, certain legal formalities had to be taken. This was to effect the closure or 'extinguishment' of highways. When an area of ground that has been a public highway (i.e. used by the general public 'as of right' over a period of, perhaps, many years) is to be restored for purposes of development, a notice has to be published to that effect in the press and notices posted on the site of the highway in question. These notices indicate the proposal by the local authority to make an Order to extinguish the highway for certain purposes, and opportunity is given during the ensuing weeks for any objections to be raised. These are later considered and, if not resolved, a public inquiry is held by a government-appointed inspector. In due course he makes his report to the Minister who either confirms the Order or quashes it.

It can be seen that in the Sidwell Street area a considerable number of highways (i.e., roads, courts, alleys, etc.) had to be dealt with and the legal work involved was indeed no small matter.

Redevelopment

In the Sidwell Street area the land, though devastated over a large area, contained isolated blocks of cottages or light industrial premises, but their positions were sporadic and it was only by piecemeal development that rebuilding could take place to allow the minimum of disturbance.

A large open area was situated at the southern end, i.e. near Clifton Road. In 1951–2 a large temporary car park was formed which greatly eased the parking problem of the time. The area embraced what is now The Triangle car park.

Rebuilding had commenced on the north side of Sidwell Street between the church and York Road.

The first road work undertaken in the area was at Acland Terrace (now Acland Road). Acland Terrace was formerly accessible by a quiet road and path, but the new roadway afforded business access, and a turning space was formed where Woolworth (currently a carpet showroom) were building their new premises near St Sidwell's Church.

Unlike the High Street area, where all sewers were first laid before any road construction, in the Sidwell Street and Fore Street areas the new

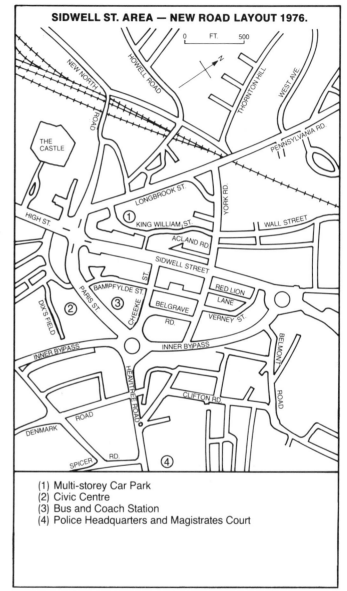

SIDWELL ST. AREA — NEW ROAD LAYOUT 1976.

(1) Multi-storey Car Park
(2) Civic Centre
(3) Bus and Coach Station
(4) Police Headquarters and Magistrates Court

sewers were laid at the same time and in the same contract as the various roadworks for each street.

Leighton Terrace car park was constructed in 1953 after 2400 cubic yards of filling had been tipped to level the site.

In looking at the section of Sidwell Street between St Sidwell's Church and Debenhams on the north side — and a similar section on the south side – one might think that the redevelopment took place on the site of bombed property. This is not so. The former buildings were, for the most part, rather old and obsolete and they were therefore demolished for new development to take place to link up the newly built Sidwell Street and Eastgate.

The buildings on opposing sides of the street were set back to allow for an overall width of 74 ft – enough for a dual carriageway, as in High Street. The dualling was, however, not carried out so the roadway was not widened. It seems that the Ministry of Transport may by then have had doubts about authorizing a dual carriageway in Sidwell Street at this point. The present kerb on the south side of Sidwell Street is therefore virtually on the same line as it was before, though previously the footpaths here were only 7–8 ft wide, despite the fact that a scheme for the widening of Sidwell Street was prepared as early as 1950!

It will also be observed that, to the rear of the north side of Sidwell Street, not only has a multi-storey car park been constructed but an area for unloading has also been provided in connection with the shops fronting Sidwell Street. This took place in the late 1960s and does not form part of the present narrative of the twenty-year period (1945-65) under review.

1960. Eastgate crossroads scheme in operation

Sidwell Street, looking towards Eastgate from Cheeke Street (This is before the widening and shows the limit of the bomb damage; St Sidwell's churchyard is just visible on right)

EIGHTEEN
The Inner Bypass

The Inner Bypass

First Section
(Belmont Road to Summerland Street)

In 1954/55 work started on the first section of the inner bypass, from Belmont Road to Summerland Street. There was at first standing property on the Belmont Road/Sidwell Street corner and the bypass therefore merged into Belmont Road for the time being so that the properties could remain undisturbed.

The proposal was ultimately for a dual carriageway from Sidwell Street right through to Exe Bridge but, in the intervening years, the whole road has not been dualled owing to restrictions of finance. Even so, the single carriageway, as we now know it, was to take successive years to accomplish as and when funds and Ministry approvals allowed.

Second Section
(Summerland Street to Paris Street)

In 1955/56 a second length of the inner bypass was begun. This extended from Summerland Street to Paris Street and the roundabout.

At this time also the construction of Verney Street and Red Lion Lane took place. Succeeding years were to see the start of improvements at York Road, Cheeke Street, Bampfylde Street — in sections at a time — and in 1959 the widening of Summerland Street.

The completion of the inner bypass section from Sidwell Street/ Belmont Road to Paris Street was, at the time, a great success in keeping needless through traffic away from Sidwell Street. This section of the bypass included the roundabout at the lower end of Paris Street, and for this to be constructed it was necessary for some isolated small cottage property to be vacated, a small burial ground to be cleared and some small light industrial premises to be relocated.

Third Section
(Paris Street to Magdalen Bridge)

1957/58 saw the start of construction of the third successive length of the inner bypass. Magdalen Bridge was so-called because that section of Magdalen Road at Fairpark did indeed have an archway affording a link between the Bull Meadow Pleasure Ground and the low-lying ground now known as Fairpark car park.

This car park was formerly an orchard and on its flank tons and tons of material from the central areas had been tipped in previous years to form an embankment. This embankment was to form the basis of construction of the bypass road and was about 15 ft above the general ground level.

In addition to the masses of material dumped from excavated

1962. Widening of Frog Street, as seen from New Bridge Street

1963. Further progress in Frog Street widening
(24 in. gas main laid alongside garage development)

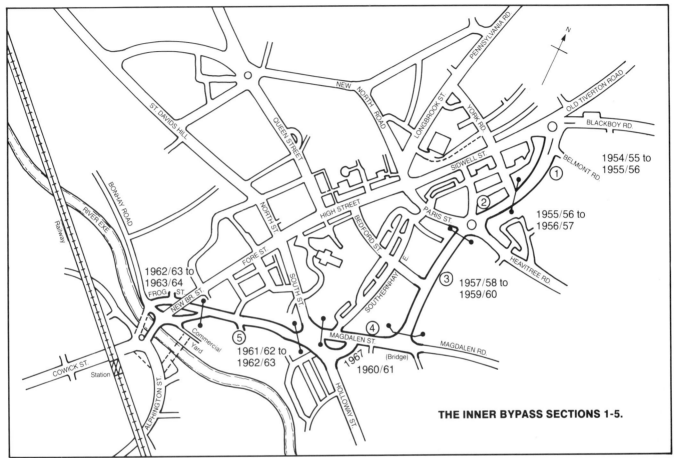

THE INNER BYPASS SECTIONS 1-5.

1954/55 to 1955/56

1955/56 to 1956/57

1957/58 to 1959/60

1962/63 to 1963/64

1961/62 to 1962/63

1967

1960/61

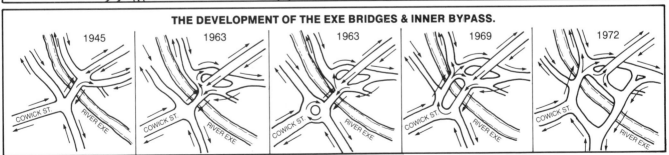

THE DEVELOPMENT OF THE EXE BRIDGES & INNER BYPASS.

1945 1963 1963 1969 1972

basements and the low-level service road, this length of road was to be partly in cutting as well. Along the Archibald Road length, the roadway was excavated in cutting and further filling was thus provided as required along the 'built-up' Fairpark length to give an easier gradient than the original ground contours would have allowed.

Before the archway beneath Magdalen Road was filled to its soffit with stone pitching, a new drainage scheme called the Larkbeare Main Drainage Scheme had commenced. It was to alleviate flooding in this valley and to provide adequate and up-to-date surface-water drainage in the whole of the Larkbeare drainage area. The large-size pipes (4½ ft diameter) were laid through the Fairpark orchard ground and through the archway to Bull Meadow. This took place in 1958/59 as part of the extensive drainage programme; and indeed it was followed the next year by another very large improvement scheme known as the Longbrook Main Drainage Scheme.

It will thus be noted that by 1959 the inner bypass had been constructed – as a single, not dual, carriageway – from Belmont Road to Magdalen Road. Much city-bound traffic could therefore be intercepted before reaching High Street and Sidwell Street. The latest section ran right through Barnfield Road and premises on each side of this road had to be demolished to make way. In addition, the lower section of Barnfield Road where it joined the inner bypass was the subject of legal proceedings for a road closure. This was a safety measure, since a four-road intersection would have been very dangerous with no signal control.

1961. Frog Street bridge before reconstruction, looking up towards New Bridge Street

1961. New Bridge Street: a start is made on the reconstruction of Frog Street Bridge

Fourth Section
(Magdalen Street/Holloway Street junction)

Traffic could therefore now skirt the city centre and, by using the existing Magdalen Street, reach the junction of Holloway Street, and South Street. This junction became a very congested one, not only with the narrow carriageway opposite the Eye Infirmary, but particularly at the Holloway Street junction.

Here a public convenience was situated below ground and in the centre of the road at the mouth of Magdalen Street. A public house on the corner of Holloway Street and Magdalen Street, known as The Valiant Soldier, became a well-known landmark in consequence — much like

the Acorn Inn is today — and traffic congestion at the Valiant Soldier became a byword.

Nearby was a long-established cycle firm named Warne, whose premises were not affected by the first corner improvement when The Valiant Soldier had to be demolished. It did, however, succumb to a later widening of the corner and there was some regret at the passing of these specimen buildings of a former age.

In the general corner improvement the public conveniences were of course demolished, filled in and the space used for extra carriageway width. Much apparatus of statutory undertakings' services was situated below ground, which made road improvements a costly and complex business.

This period was 1960–61. The natural consequence was that the

1962. Frog Street bridge: the complication of underground services

final link from Holloway Street to Exe Bridge should thereafter be undertaken to complete the route between Sidwell Street and the River Exe.

1959. The old Cowick Street at its junction with Alphington Street

Fifth Section
(Holloway Street to Exe Bridge)

In connection with this section of the inner bypass – and before the bypass could become properly effective – it was necessary to improve the Frog Street arch bridge that carried New Bridge Street overhead. Here there was an existing ready-made two-level crossroads system, but Frog Street at that time was narrow and little used. If was planned to use this facility to turn traffic movements to advantage by means of this two-tier cross-over.

Only one Exe Bridge existed at this time and a considerable proportion of traffic entering the city from the St Thomas side of the river (including holiday traffic in season) used to turn right from Exe Bridge into what was then Commercial Road, along the northern side of the river. This inward flow met the outward-flowing traffic coming down New Bridge Street hill to the bridge and was controlled by traffic signals. Facilities for the right-hand-turning traffic meant holding back the opposing traffic stream with consequent bad, very delaying congestion at peak times.

By improving Frog Street Bridge, the incoming traffic at Exe Bridge could be turned *left* to cross New Bridge Street's traffic flow *beneath* New Bridge Street; this made an immediate and remarkable improvement when completed.

As a prerequisite to this 'gyratory' traffic system, it was necessary to

1960. Demolition begins in Cowick Street

widen, or rather to reconstruct, the existing bridge, giving Frog Street a wider carriageway beneath New Bridge Street. This was carried out in 1961–2 and was done in two halves to minimize interference with traffic flows. At the same time a start was made at the Holloway Street end of the inner bypass and the section to Frog Street was opened to traffic on 20 December 1962.

Where the new inner bypass crossed over the old Coombe Street, about 6 ft depth of filling was required. This automatically converted Coombe Street into a cul-de-sac and enabled the construction of a pedestrian subway to link with lower Coombe Street on the other side of the inner bypass. A 24 in. diameter C.I. gas main had to be laid along this length of bypass and the weather caused severe hold-ups to construction.

The roadway, cutting obliquely across the old City Wall at this point, regrettably meant the removal of a large section of this ancient monument. Authority was, however, given by the then Ministry of Works, following the usual procedures of recording data.

Frog Street 'underpass' was opened to traffic in 1963 and by 1964 the section from Holloway Street right through to Exe Bridge (save for asphalt surfacing) was completed.

The General Functioning of the Inner Bypass

There was now a most valuable link from Sidwell Street to Exe Bridge and in 1962/63 the roundabout at Sidwell Street/Blackboy Road was constructed to facilitate traffic flow at this intersection. This involved the demolition of some property and the demolition and later relocation of the underground conveniences and the fountain which lent its name to the old junction at this time.

Much traffic congestion did, however, occur at Magdalen Street/ Holloway Street junction and near the now relocated Acorn Inn. There had been constructed in 1965 a short service road at the rear of the new Acorn Inn which was to serve for unloading purposes. The original proposal was that this service road would later be extended to reach

1962. Widening of Cowick Street, facing Exe Bridge

future residential units adjoining the Acorn. This, however, did not materialize and, after some study of traffic conditions, the service road was extended, strengthened and was destined to become a main road as part of the inner bypass system.

Thus, in about 1967, was introduced the present gyratory traffic system around the Acorn site, which over recent years has been widened again to take increased volumes of circulating traffic.

In about 1966/67, attention was turned again to Exe Bridge — the only substantial crossing point over the River Exe for miles.

One side of Cowick Street, on the St Thomas side of the river, had been demolished in 1962 (from the River Exe to the railway bridge) and the area at the bridge head was ripe for redevelopment. This section of Cowick Street was widened in 1963 and a small roundabout was constructed to regulate traffic flow at the important junction with Alphington Street.

The natural sequence of events was therefore the construction of a new Exe Bridge North, which was opened in 1969. This operated a gyratory traffic system with the existing Exe Bridge — like a roundabout spanning the river.

Then, in 1972, a second new bridge — Exe Bridge South — was completed. This bridge was located on the downstream side of the old Exe Bridge to form a greater gyratory system with longer weaving lengths for traffic. Subways were built for pedestrians and, once the two new bridges were fully operational, proposals were formulated for the demolition of the old Exe Bridge, a steel-arched bridge that had been in operation since 1905.

1963. Completion of widening of Cowick Street

NINETEEN

The Flooding of 1960

The Flooding of 1960

The low-lying areas of Exwick and St Thomas were subject to flooding dangers in times of heavy and sustained rainfall. It was not uncommon for flood-waters to spread across the Exwick playing fields, so a constant watch on river levels was maintained in case the need for sandbagging arose.

In 1953/54, therefore, a new Station Road Bridge was constructed, bringing the road to a higher level above the flood-waters, and at the same time allowing water to pass beneath its open spans. Hitherto Station Road stood on a low embankment across the fields of Exwick, and this prevented flood-water from flowing away.

In 1960, however, both in October and in December severe flooding occurred on the River Exe. Many houses were flooded and damage and misery were widespread in Exwick and St Thomas in particular. The dreary business of drying out the houses was helped by the use of mechanical driers hired from the services. Many firms assisted in the drying of carpets and so on.

Construction of Exwick Floodbank

It was determined at once to form a flood-bank along the perimeter of the Exwick fields. All the excavated material from the central areas, whether from basement excavation for shops, excavation for sewers or from roadworks was diverted to Exwick. Lorry after lorry deposited its load under supervision to form a bank 8 ft high and 10–12 ft wide. Even this was not sufficient to maintain the progress required, so tons of hardcore had to be purchased in addition to enable the work to proceed.

Further flooding occurred in 1962 but, happily, the Exwick flood-bank held the water and, by comparison with two years before, the damage done was much less.

The story of the flooding could be a narrative in itself, but this brief reference is included here because of its impact on the work going on in the city at this time. There is little doubt that the improvements carried out in the drainage areas of the Larkbeare and Longbrook valleys between 1958 and 1962 did much to eliminate problems in many areas of the city that were prone to flooding because of the over-charged or small-capacity sewers that existed previously.

Flooding at Exe Bridge

Conclusion

The construction of the two new Exe Bridges (Exe Bridge North and Exe Bridge South) has not been described here in detail, being outside the scope of the initial reconstruction scheme.

The main capital works undertakings have been listed, however, from 1966 to 1974. This completes the sequence of events leading to the winding-up of the old City Council before the great reorganization of local government in April 1974.

It would seem that reconstruction of the central areas following the ravages of the war virtually terminated in 1965/66. It was in 1966 that the extension of the city's boundaries brought Topsham, Pinhoe and Alphington into Exeter. General reconstruction gave way to a series of capital works projects both in the civil engineering and architectural fields.

From 1965 onwards a gradual change came over the central administration and operation of local government. New road markings were introduced, main route numbers were changed and a reclassification of highways took place. The concept of Traffic Management emerged, with the introduction of traffic wardens, yellow lines, one-way streets, prohibition of waiting in streets, etc. Traffic Engineering evolved from the collection of data on traffic counts and movement and estimated growth.

Then there emerged working parties, forward planning, conservation, public participation, and a whole host of new words and studies were brought into use. These included economic assessments, feasibility studies, in-depth examination, critical path analysis, viable proposals and housing yardsticks. Management began to take over the reins; work studies on aspects of all departments took place; manpower grew accordingly. Project Planners and Project Co-ordinators were appointed to feed back information for consideration in the new corporate management structure.

These processes naturally had a great slowing-down effect, but some will doubtless argue that in more recent times, though progress may be slower, the public at large are made aware earlier of the Council's proposals and are given a chance to comment upon them. One may well contemplate how progress in reconstruction after the end of the war may have been affected had the more recent multi-sided considerations been brought into play at that time.

Sketch of the proposed Civic Centre building

TWENTY

Outline of Other Development in the Early Years

Housing

The provision of housing to compensate for the losses in the war and to catch up with arrears was embarked upon concurrently with the widespread development in the city centre.

Building was started on a 60 acre site at Stoke Hill. Then in 1949, the then Princess Elizabeth, while in Exeter to unveil the plaque at Princesshay, also went to Toronto House to open officially Homes for the Aged, built under the Lord Mayor of London's National Air Raid Distress Fund Scheme. This housing estate had new schools incorporated in the development and, later, a 13 acre site of allotments in the centre of the area was also developed by the city for houses and flats. All estates were of course served by new roads and sewers, lighting, utility services and cleansing.

At Countess Wear another 100 acre estate was developed, with schools and shopping centre, and a further Council housing estate of 100 acres was developed at Whipton Barton North and Whipton Barton South. These were permanent houses as distinct from the temporary housing at such other sites as Bramley Avenue, Birchy Barton Hill, Hamlyn Gardens and Abbeville Close. By 1975, however, these latter sites had been redeveloped for permanent housing.

Schools

Clearly the 1950s and 1960s were years of great activity, not only for housing with schools embodied within the neighbourhood created, but also for such 'separate' schools as Vincent Thompson School for 450 boys and the Priory School for 450 girls, designed by the Council.

Other schools were constructed at Stoke Hill, St James at Summer Lane, Whipton Barton, and St Thomas, amongst others. Of course, many other schools, colleges, libraries, etc. have since been built, as well as the Police Station, Magistrates Court, Library and Technical College. But it is really with the period from 1945 to 1965 that this narrative mainly deals.

Industry

One of Sharp's recommendations was the creation of an industrial area on land to the south of the city to accommodate warehouses and factories blitzed in the war and to provide alternative sites for obsolete or badly sited premises. It was also intended to attract industry to Exeter.

Toronto House old people's home

Stoke Hill housing estate, 1949–58

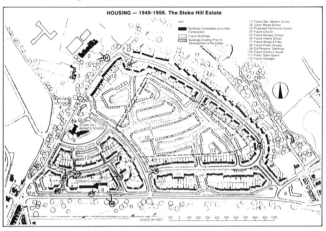

HOUSING — 1949-1958. The Stoke Hill Estate

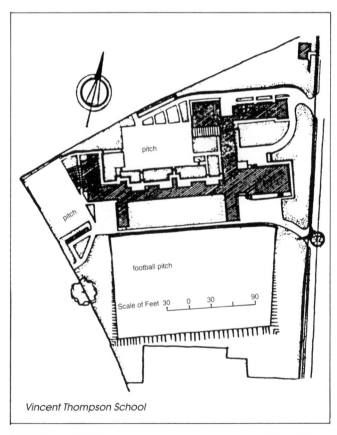

Vincent Thompson School

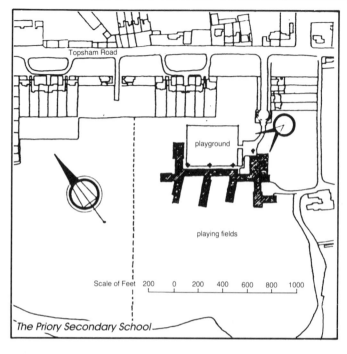

The Priory Secondary School

Marsh Barton

And so it was that in 1948 the Council acquired the first instalment of land – some 48 acres – and this was quickly taken up. Formerly the land was occupied by a greyhound stadium and by an orchard and grazing land owned by a farmer, Mr Newberry. Here again, the sewers had to be designed to take the estimated storm water and foul sewage from the premises likely to be sited there. Following the sewers, roads were constructed and also a branch line from the railway.

The industrial site grew over the years until in 1971 it was well over five times as large. A further extension of land totalling 47 acres was subsequently acquired south of the Clapper Brook (the then Devon River Authority's flood channel). A new bridge was completed in 1974, spanning the flood channel, and was planned to be the main access to this area from the rest of the estate.

Pinhoe

In addition to Marsh Barton, an area of some 14 acres in the Venny Bridge area at Pinhoe was acquired and this has been fully developed. The site is near the A38 main road which is ideal for road communication and, before the M5, was the chief access road to the west. Exhibition Way was constructed for only half its width, pending a future link-up over the railway to land to the north.

Sowton

The City Council's other venture on the industrial front was to combine with Devon County Council in the financing of roads and sewers on a site at Sowton. The construction side was carried out by Devon County Council. The site — of 60 acres — is close to the main Sidmouth road A3052 and the M5 motorway.

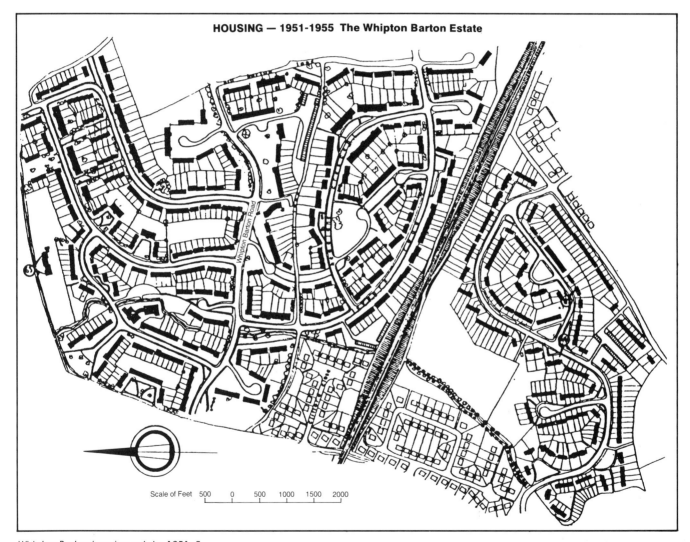

HOUSING — 1951-1955 The Whipton Barton Estate

Scale of Feet   500   0   500   1000   1500   2000

Whipton Barton housing estate, 1951–5

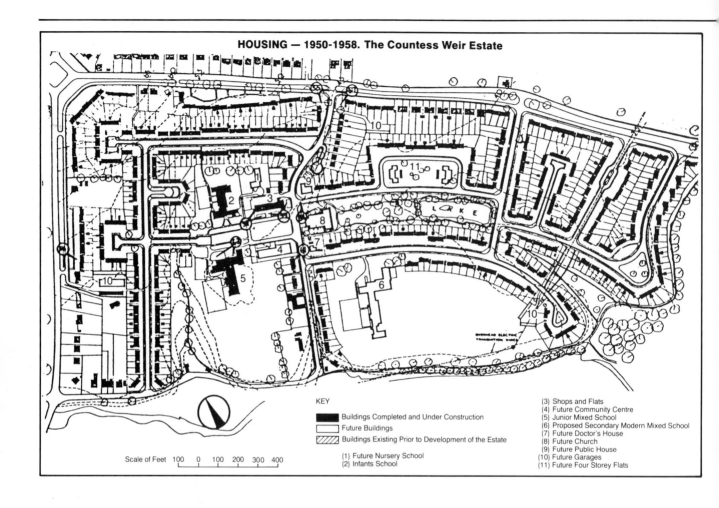

HOUSING — 1950-1958. The Countess Weir Estate

KEY

Buildings Completed and Under Construction
Future Buildings
Buildings Existing Prior to Development of the Estate

(1) Future Nursery School
(2) Infants School

(3) Shops and Flats
(4) Future Community Centre
(5) Junior Mixed School
(6) Proposed Secondary Modern Mixed School
(7) Future Doctor's House
(8) Future Church
(9) Future Public House
(10) Future Garages
(11) Future Four Storey Flats

Scale of Feet   100   0   100   200   300   400

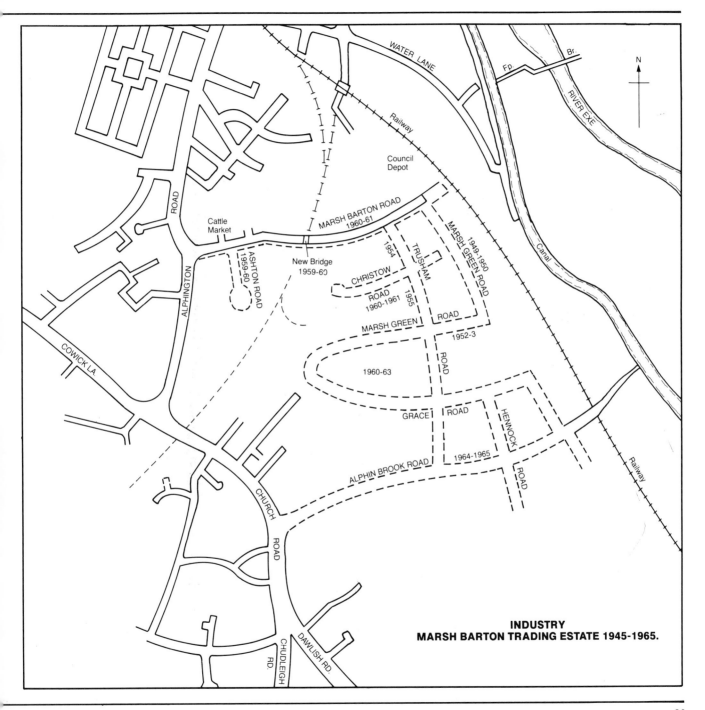

INDUSTRY
MARSH BARTON TRADING ESTATE 1945-1965.

PART 2

General Summary of Progress
Year by Year, 1945–65

General Summary of Progress Year by Year, 1945–65

1945/46

Thomas Sharp, Town Planning Consultant, prepared his Survey and Proposals for the redevelopment of Exeter. His proposals were set out in a book *Exeter Phoenix* (published by The Architectural Press), so named after the fabulous bird that arose from the ashes of destruction.

1946/47

Details of Sharp's plans and proposals were displayed at a public exhibition held in the ruined City Library. Later in the year a public inquiry was held in the Guildhall to consider the compulsory purchase of war-damaged areas, for redevelopment by the City Council.

1947/48

High Street area, etc. Land surveys of the blitzed areas were prepared and drawn to a large scale for detailed proposals to be formulated.
Temporary shops were approved for erection at Eastgate and Fore Street areas.
Inner bypass. Alternative schemes for routes north of city centre (Sharp's plan) and south of city centre were prepared. The latter had the advantage on cost; it also intercepted the bulk of traffic arriving from the east, before it reached the central area.

1948/49

Temporary shops were erected at Eastgate on derelict land adjacent to the Co-operative Society building. These faced towards the Cathedral. The shops also extended on to both sides of Southernhay where this road at that time emerged on to Eastgate. The shops were of pre-cast concrete construction. Temporary Shops were also erected at Fore Street on the site of the ruined lower market.
General tidying up of blitzed sites was undertaken by Council labour, including removal of emergency static water tanks.
Mr John Brierley was appointed City Engineer & Surveyor following the earlier retirement of Mr R. H. Dymond. Mr Brierley was to continue as City Engineer for the next twenty-four years.
The design of sewers in the central area commenced and the preparation of a contract for the work followed. Building licences were made available and the first allocation was made for steel, for 300 tons. Sites for development could now be let and Pearl Assurance House in High Street was the first site to be let.
HOUSING. Various schemes for prefabricated dwellings were in course of preparation and construction.
INDUSTRY. Marsh Barton Trading Estate site approved and plans and contract to be prepared following land acquisition for first stage of development (viz. Marsh Green Road, as it was later to be named).

1949/50

Inner bypass. The southern alternative route was finally approved by the City Council and the then Ministry of Transport. The general road layout for the central area could therefore be formulated now that this major issue had been settled.
Commemorative Feature, pedestrian shopping street, designed and constructed by the City Council before work on the new road proposals had commenced. H.R.H. Princess Elizabeth unveiled a plaque on 21 October 1949 and named the street 'Princesshay'.
High Street area. (This area, frequently referred to, includes Catherine St, Bailey St, Musgrave Row, Bedford St, Princesshay, Post Office St, Bluecoat Lane.) Contract for laying foul and surface-water sewers commenced July 1949.
Catherine Street. Underground conveniences – design received approval of the then Ministry of Health.
6 000 cubic yards of rubble from excavations by developers taken to the Larkbeare Valley at Barnfield as filling for embankment for the future inner by-pass.
Traffic counts were taken to formulate proposals for the main road layout in the central area. Considerable negotiations with statutory undertakings. Legal plans for land acquisition and procedures for road closures.
New car park at Mary Arches Street was opened; the car park at Paul Street was closed to private cars owing to demand for larger coach station site.
HOUSING. Work to the value of £40 000 completed for roads on various housing estates.
INDUSTRY. Marsh Barton Trading Estate – the first contract for roads and sewers (£16 000) was completed (i.e. first section of Marsh Green Road).
Pinhoe Trading Estate – contract in course of preparation.

1950/51

High Street area. First (main sewers) contract completed (£28 000). Second (roads and drainage) contract (£40 000) started September 1950.
Catherine Street. Underground conveniences – contractor appointed but start delayed to allow construction of Catherine Street to approach completion.
Inner bypass. Route surveyed from Sidwell Street to Exe Bridge (estimated cost £815 000).
4000 cubic yards excavated rubble taken to Barnfield for future inner by-pass construction.
Sidwell Street and Southernhay. Schemes prepared for improvements.
Car parking. Report approved by City Council for providing not less than 4000 car park spaces.
>*Bystock Green.* New car park constructed and improved with flower-beds.
>*Leighton Terrace.* Compulsory purchase order approved and rubble tipped to form level site.

Fore Street and New Bridge Street closed for reconstruction of carriageway surface; day and night work.

HOUSING.   Work proceeding at Stoke Hill and Countess Wear estates. Schemes prepared for Whipton Barton area including George's Chapel Fields.

INDUSTRY.   Marsh Barton – extension of contract for further roads and sewers for new development sites.

Pinhoe Trading Estate – further work undertaken (£18400) on preparation of layout.

1951/52

High Street area.   Second contract roads and sewers (Bailey St, Musgrave Road, Bedford St, Catherine St, Post Office St, etc.) reached final stages.

Princesshay partially paved at north end (Singer's, etc.) frontage.

Catherine Street conveniences neared completion save for fittings and treatment of flower-bed over.

Southernhay.   Two surface car parks being constructed on blitzed sites (This is now replaced by Broadwalk House.)

Leighton Terrace car park started. 2400 cubic yards of filling used for levelling the site.

Large temporary car park formed on south side of Sidwell Street greatly eases parking problems. Now taken over as The Triangle car park.

Traffic counts taken at Exe Bridge to determine future widths of approach roads.

Institution of Municipal Engineers.   Meeting at Guildhall. Mr Brierley, City Engineer, read a paper 'The Reconstruction in the City of Exeter'. Meeting attended by the President of the Institution and representatives of many local authorities throughout the country. VIsit to site and plans on view.

HOUSING.   Stoke Hill and Countess Wear progressing well as also at Whipton Barton South, Whipton Lane and Vaughan Road. Further contracts at Whipton Barton North, including footbridge over railway, and Beacon Lane.

INDUSTRY.   Marsh Barton – a further contract started (£7260) for roads and sewers.

Pinhoe Trading Estate – roads and sewers completed for letting of all sites.

1952/53

High Street area.   Second contract (roads and sewers) completed.

Southernhay.   Two surface car parks completed.

Trinity Green.   Burial ground cleared. Construction of car park, shelter and conveniences started.

Catherine Street conveniences completed and opened to the public 22 January 1953.

Leighton Terrace car park virtually completed.

Acland Road.   Work commenced (taking its name from Acland Terrace, hitherto approached by footpath only).

Further 4500 cubic yards excavated material to Barnfield for filling for future inner bypass.

Mary Arches Street, George Street, Guinea Street, Bampfylde Street (part), Cheeke Street (part), Bude Street (part).   Improvement schemes prepared and submitted to Ministry of Transport for approval.

Station Road, Exwick.   £13000 contract started for new viaduct bridge, raising level of roadway to be above the flood level at that time.

Cowick Street.   Scheme prepared for widening (from Exe Bridge to railway bridge, St Thomas Station).

HOUSING.   Work continues at Whipton Barton South and North, Beacon Lane, Whipton Lane, Vaughan Road, Stoke Hill and Countess Wear.

1953/54

St George's Churchyard, South Street cleared of burials, prior to later road widening and shopping development buildings.

Mary Arches Street (Fore Street to car park), *George Street, Guinea Street* completed.

Bampfylde Street/Bude Street completed, in part lengths.

Trinity Green, shelter and conveniences completed and opened to the public on 31 October 1953.

High Street Arcade completed.

Acland Road completed.

Additional 7000 cubic yards excavated material to Barnfield for proposed inner bypass.

South Street (Fore Street to Coombe Street), *Fore Street* (South Street to Market Street).   Schemes prepared and submitted to Ministry of Transport for approval (estimate £31000).

Inner bypass, Stage I (Belmont Road to Summerland Street).   Scheme submitted to Ministry of Transport for approval (estimate £12000).

Counts of parked vehicles in central area.

Seven-day census of traffic at Exe Bridge at Ministry of Transport's request.

Station Road, Exwick.   Viaduct completed.

1954/55

Southernhay.   One-way traffic in Southernhay East and West introduced in April 1954.

South Street widening (Fore Street to Coombe Street) started.

Fore Street widening (South Street to Market Street) started.

Inner bypass Stage I (Belmont Road to Summerland Street) started.

All the hardcore filling at Barnfield completed for later construction of the inner bypass (See 1957/58).

Verney Street, Red Lion Lane.   Schemes prepared for approval.

Bedford Street, Catherine Street, Castle Street.   'No Waiting' and limited waiting signs erected.

HOUSING.   Work proceeding on the large estates at Countess Wear, Stoke Hill and Whipton areas.

1955/56

South Street Stage I (Fore Street to Coombe Street) completed.
Fore Street (South Street to Market Street) in progress).
Inner bypass Stage 1 (Belmont Road to Summerland Street) completed.
Inner bypass Stage 2 (Summerland Street to Paris Street and Roundabout) started.
Verney Street started.
Red Lion Lane started.
Eastgate Square. Alternative Schemes prepared for treatment of junction.
South Street Stage 2. (Coombe Street to Magdalen Street). Scheme prepared and submitted to Ministry of Transport for approval.
HOUSING. Progress maintained and additional works started at Beacon Lane North and at Heavitree Bridge.
INDUSTRY. Marsh Barton — completion of paths as site development proceeds. Turning space for buses formed at Ashton Road opposite cattle market.

1956/57

Fore Street widening completed (South Street to Market Street).
Inner bypass Stage 2 (Summerland Street to Paris Street and roundabout) completed.
Red Lion Lane completed.
Verney Street completed.
York Road (Sidwell Street to Acland Road) started (estimated cost £6 500).
Princesshay nearing completion, including arcade.
Eastgate (a) Scheme for roundabout. (b) Scheme for crossroads and traffic signals. Considered by City Council who selected (b) for submission to Ministry of Transport.
Exe Bridge. Scheme for new Exe Bridge and 'Underpass' at Frog Street submitted to Ministry of Transport (£605 000).
Cheeke Street, Belgrave Road. Scheme for extension of these roads submitted to Ministry of Transport for approval in connection with the construction of the proposed Bus and Coach Station, Paris Street.
Cowick Street. Widening scheme prepared in detail (Exe Bridge to railway bridge). Scheme later held in abeyance.
INDUSTRY. Further extension works at Marsh Barton.

1957/58

South Street Stage 2 (Coombe Street to Magdalen Street) almost completed.
York Road (Sidwell Street to Acland Road) completed.
Princesshay Arcade completed.
Inner bypass Stage 3 (Paris Street to Magdalen Bridge) started.
Cheeke Street extension started.
Eastgate. Ministry of Transport approve scheme for crossroads and traffic signals. Detailed drawings prepared.

Paris Street. Realignment at Eastgate approved.
Summerland Street. Widening scheme prepared and submitted to Ministry of Transport for approval (£25 000).
Gyratory traffic scheme for High St, Queen St, Paul St, North St submitted to Ministry of Transport for approval.
MAIN DRAINAGE. Larkbeare drainage scheme prepared (£190 000). Submitted to Ministry of Housing and Local Government for approval. Public inquiry at Guildhall; no objections.
HOUSING. Dunsford Road estate contract started.
INDUSTRY. Marsh Barton — extension of trading estate continues.

Princesshay

1958/59

Cheeke Street extension completed.
Inner bypass Stage 3 (Paris Street to Magdalen Bridge) completed.
Summerland Street widening started.
Eastgate and Paris Street work started.
Paris Street to Post Office Street link road started.
Bedford Street. Footpath works to completed properties.
Paris Street area. Various properties being demolished by the Council in readiness for future Bus and Coach Station.
Car Parks. Temporary car parks completed at The Triangle, Dix's Field, Belmont Road, Coombe Street.
Underground Passages. New entrance at Princesshay. Scheme prepared.

The following schemes prepared and submitted for M.o.T. approval:
Bartholomew Street East and *Mary Arches Street* (at Bartholomew Street end).
New Service Road (Gater Lane) off Palace Gate.

Cowick Street (Exe Bridge to railway bridge) including rear service access.

MAIN DRAINAGE. Larkbeare scheme approved and started. Longbrook scheme (£188 000) submitted for approval.

HOUSING. Contracts completed at Stoke Hill, Countess Wear and Dunsford Road estates; Beacon Lane progressing.

1959/60

Inner bypass Stage 3 (Paris Street to Magdalen Bridge) completed.
Eastgate crossroads completed save for asphalt surfacing.
Paris Street to Post Office Street link road completed.
Summerland Street completed.
Castle Street. Demolitions in Little Castle Street to remove bottleneck at Bailey Street.
Gandy Street. Demolition of properties to link Musgrave Row with Gandy Street and Queen Street.
Paris Street area. Further demolitions for Bus Station site.
Cheeke Street completed.
Bedford Street. New surface-water sewer laid opposite to the Post Office prior to paving of forecourts and flower-beds.
Bartholomew Street East widening started.
Underground Passages. Entrance completed in Princesshay.
Gater Lane (at Palace Gate). Service access completed.
Cowick Street. A small roundabout constructed on south side of river as interim traffic scheme. Widening scheme was deferred pending vacation of premises and alternative accommodation provided for Alphington Street/Cowick Street junction.
MAIN DRAINAGE. Larkbeare scheme progressing; Longbrook scheme approved and contract let.
HOUSING
Barley Mount estate. Work in progress (roads and sewers).
Chestnut Avenue, Bovemoors Lane. Two contracts let for construction of footpaths and verges.
INDUSTRY. Marsh Barton – Contract no. 10 for roads and sewers completed, forming Christow Road and Ashton Road. Old railway bridge over Marsh Barton Road replaced by welded girder bridge on Sunday 13 March 1960.

1960/61

Eastgate and Paris Street completed.
High Street widening (Eastgate to Curry's) started.
Princesshay. Paving between High Street and Post Office Street complete. Special treatment in crazy paving of site of demolished City Wall.
Temporary shops. Last of the temporary shops demolished.
Bedford Street. Paving to forecourts completed, including low-level forecourt, steps and ramped path.
South Street. 'Piazza' and new access way to Cathedral Yard including service area at rear of shops in South Street. Permanent flagged paving laid to newly erected shops (on the Cathedral side).
One-way gyratory traffic scheme in High St, Queen St, Paul St, and North St brought into operation at midnight Sunday, 22 November 1960. Abandoned after twenty-two days owing to danger to pedestrians at congested spots. (One such instance was at Cornish's North Street corner, where narrow width of footpath prevented the erection of guard rails.)
Floods. Serious flooding in October and December 1960 at Exwick and St Thomas. All available hardcore to Exwick for construction of flood-bank. Much hardcore had to be purchased for the work to proceed. Provision of soil and planting was also started at the flood-bank.
Magdalen Street/South Street junction. Old public convenience in centre of road demolished for corner improvement. New traffic lights installed at this ('Valiant Soldier') junction.
St Katherine's Almshouses. Ruins laid out as a memorial, grassed, lighted and provided with seats.
Southernhay widened opposite the former hospital site. 'No Waiting' and 'Limited Waiting' introduced for the whole of Southernhay.
Car parking. Variable scale parking charges introduced at: Trinity Green, Smythen St, Central Station, Leighton Terrace, Mary Arches St and Southernhay. Kiosks and barriers erected to control entry.
Large 'free' parks provided at The Triangle, Fairpark and Coombe St.
Demolition of old Court House and police buildings, Waterbeer St, to make room for temporary car park at Pancras Lane (now the site of Guildhall Shopping Centre). Old almshouses at Bartholomew Street East also demolished.
Frog Street/New Bridge Street. Tender accepted for a new bridge (for inner bypass to pass underneath). Fine Arts Commission approves.
Schemes in preparation: inner bypass (Holloway Street to Bonhay Road) and new roundabout at Blackboy Road/Sidwell Street.
Service road and car park to serve rear of new Paris Street (south side) shops.
MAIN DRAINAGE. Larkbeare scheme completed in April 1960. Longbrook scheme started in June by the same contractors. Larkbeare scheme had proved itself as no flooding took place in this area during the heavy storms at the end of 1960.
HOUSING. Barley Lane and Beacon Lane estates completed. Bovemoors Lane and Chestnut Avenue proceeding.
INDUSTRY. Marsh Green Road extended. Completion of Christow Road. Widening of Marsh Barton Road.

1961/62

High Street (Eastgate to Curry's) completed.
Service access rear of Paris Street completed.
Princesshay. Last paving completed.
Bluecoat Lane service road rear of Post Office completed.
Market Street widening completed.
Demolition between Eastgate and Longbrook Street completed. This

1962. Blackboy Road roundabout in course of construction (Note old Blackboy Road now converted into layby)

enabled a start to be made on the *service area rear of Debenhams,* and developers could proceed with the main building.

Inner bypass (Holloway Street to Exe Bridge) started.

Frog Street Bridge (New Bridge Street) started. Work done in two halves. New Bridge Street closed to down traffic. Work complicated by 4000 pairs G.P.O. cables, two water mains, and two 15in gas mains. Cost of alterations to mains was 14% of the contract sum (£60,000).

Sidwell Street roundabout started.

Blackboy Road dual carriageway started.

Cowick Street/Alphington Street. Demolition of corner premises to enable widening of Cowick Street to proceed.

MAIN DRAINAGE. Longbrook surface-water scheme completed.

INDUSTRY. Pinhoe Trading Estate – verges and paths all completed.

CLIFTON HILL. Scheme prepared for running track on site of old filling to quarry.

1962/63

Service area rear of Debenhams completed. Paving in front of Debenhams completed.

Sidwell Street roundbout progressing.

Blackboy Road dual carriageway completed.

Bude Street (off Bampfylde Street) service road to premises in Sidwell Street started.

1962. View across the site of the proposed Bus and Coach Station towards Paris Street and Southernhay

Inner bypass (Holloway Street to Exe Bridge) proceeding, but severe winter weather held up progress for some weeks. Holloway Street to Frog Street opened to traffic 20 December 1962.

Frog Street. Demolitions at Beal's Garage. 350ft of higher leat culverted with twin 48 in. pipes.

Cricklepit Street. 25ft high retaining wall built along flank of inner bypass.

MAIN DRAINAGE. The St Thomas main drainage scheme started (new surface water sewers over a wide area).

HOUSING. Work in progress at Wellington Road and at Weirfield Road.

INDUSTRY. Extension of Marsh Green Road completed. Bridford Road completed. Survey for extension further south to Clapperbrook Lane (now named Alphin Brook Road).

1963/64

Inner bypass (Holloway Street to Bonhay Road) completed save for asphalt surfacing and subway finishes.

Frog Street 'underpass' opened to traffic 14 June 1963.

One-way traffic gyratory system north of Exe Bridge introduced 3 July 1963. This made use of the underpass and there was instant easing of traffic congestion by the elimination of the right-hand turning of vehicles off Exe Bridge to inner bypass. Such traffic would now turn left off the bridge leaving the road clear for oncoming traffic.

Bus and Coach Station, Paris Street. Work in progress. Retaining walls virtually completed.

Market Street widened at lower market site following the demolition of the old Druid's Hall.

Bailey Street. Unsightly wall on site of old City Wall rebuilt in the Square at Northernhay Place.

Paris Street arcade paving completed.

Bude Street completed.

Service road rear of Clarendon House in course of preparation and to be known as Russell Street. Clarendon House in course of erection.

Car parks constructed at Waterbeer St, Bartholomew St West, Magdalen St and Okehampton St.

Underground conveniences, Blackboy Road, nearing completion so that existing underground conveniences may be demolished. This would make way for completion of roundabout at Old Tiverton Road.

MAIN DRAINAGE. St Thomas main drainage scheme, Stage 1 completed. Stage 2 started in July 1963.

PUBLIC BUILDINGS. Magistrates Court and Police headquarters in Heavitree Road opened 10 March 1964.

1964/65

The following works were completed:

Bailey Street square.
Coombe Street subway.
Inner bypass asphalt surfacing.
Sidwell Street roundabout.
Coach Station, Paris Street.
Bude Street, service road and car park.
King William Street rear of Debenhams.
Russell Street, rear of Clarendon House.
Mary Arches Street, service access on south side.

New underground conveniences, Blackboy Road.

New North Road/Longbrook Street junction, abutting Prudential Assurance building; widening work commenced. (This site was formerly the theatre.)

Car park constructed at Lower Coombe Street.

Temporary car parks formed at Cowick Street (opposite Wardrew Road) and Cemetery Place, Iron Bridge.

Magdalen Street, Holloway Street junction. Plans prepared for a short minor service road rear of 'Acorn Inn'. Later, in 1967, this road was to become upgraded as part of gyratory link road forming part of inner bypass.

Old Bus and Coach Station, Paul Street was vacated and the site adapted for car parking.

Clifton Hill Athletic Track formed with additional sports facilities on site of old quarry, recently filled by tipping.

MAIN DRAINAGE. Second stage St Thomas main drainage scheme virtually completed.

HOUSING. Wellington Road and Weirfield Road estates virtually completed. Contracts let for Friar's Gate, Thornberry Avenue, Goldsmith Street, Heavitree estates.

INDUSTRY. Contract no. 13 for roads and sewers completed. Contract no. 14 prepared for further extension of estate to keep pace with letting of sites.

PUBLIC BUILDINGS. New City Library opened 22 October 1965.

New Technical College (Teaching Block), opened September 1965.

Summary of remaining years up to the reorganization of Local Government 1966–74

1966 Boundary extension: Exeter takes in Topsham, Pinhoe and Alphington.

1967 Demolition in Holloway Street area. Road behind the Acorn Inn linked to Holloway Street for gyratory traffic system.

1968 First stage of new sewage works at Countess Wear commenced 24 March. Refuse incinerator started at Marsh Barton. Multi-storey car park at Sidwell Street.

1969 Exe Bridge North completed and opened 30 July.

1970 New sewage works completed at Countess Wear. Refuse incinerator completed and opened in January.

1971 New Civic Centre completed (first phase); part of staff move in from Southernhay in March.

1972 Exe Bridge South completed and opened 15 May. New Civic Centre (second phase) completed. Remainder of staff move in from Southernhay in June.

1973 Bull Meadow Road proposal controversy. Scheme abandoned.

1974 Reorganization of local government. Operative date 1 April. Powers and duties of Exeter City Council considerably curtailed in favour of Devon Council Council and the newly constituted South West Water Authority.

1965. Aerial view of Sidwell Street and High Street area

PART 3:
Appendix

Some Notes on the Blitz on Exeter in 1942

Following the R.A.F. attack on Lubeck, Germany, Exeter was bombed as part of a series of retaliatory raids by the Germans on cathedral cities and places of national interest. Germany afterwards boasted that it had destroyed Exeter, 'the Jewel of the West'. Certainly Exeter paid a heavy price for being classified as one of the most beautiful cities in England.

The Raid

The raid took place on night of 3/4 May 1942. It started at 2 a.m. and lasted 1½ hours.

Full moon, clear sky, almost cloudless. Germans approached up the estuary. Incendiary bombs lit target as the first planes circled the sleeping city.

75 tons of bombs fell in 74 minutes. There were forty planes, 160 high explosives, 10000 incendiary bombs and parachute mines.

Anti-aircraft guns replied. Half an hour after first planes had dropped bombs, fighters of No. 10 Group arrived. The Polish Air Force 307 Night Fighter Squadron (the Eagles Lwow) shot down four. Blaze seen 40-50 miles away.

Shelters

About 6000 Morrison-type steel-table shelters and 476 Anderson-type corrugated-steel garden shelters in Exeter. Only one received direct hit, killing nine people.

Casualties

156 killed, 563 injured.

Bombs fell on: High St, Sidwell St, Fore St, Southernhay, South St, Paris St, Belmont Rd, Newtown, St Leonard's.

It could have been worse because some pilots dropped their bombs outside the city.

The famous Deller's Cafe was destroyed, two hotels (The Globe, in Cathedral Yard, and Seven Stars, near Exe Bridge) also were demolished.

Bombs fell on Cathedral precincts. Cathedral survived but not without some damage. In St James choir vaulting was torn away from the south choir aisle.

The new City Library with thousands of books, engulfed in flames.

St Luke's College, City Hospital, Heavitree Road, and G.P.O. in High Street hit. Telephone exchange survived.

Catherine Street, 1942

Buildings Destroyed

  9 churches
  6 banks
26 public houses
  5 off-licences
  4 chemists
  1 cinema
Over 400 shops
Nearly 150 offices
Over 50 warehouses and stores
Of 20000 houses in city, 1500 totally destroyed, 2700 seriously damaged.

Buildings Damaged in Greater or Lesser Degree

  11 schools
800 offices and warehouses
  22 churches
16000 houses, approx.

'Morrison' shelter

'Anderson' shelter

War damage: Southernhay

The Aftermath

The day after the raid was a perfect spring day.

It took the national fire service 5 hrs to bring fires under control.

Field kitchens at Bury Meadow provided refreshments for women and children.

Seventeen gas mains fractured: several weeks before supplies resumed.

Few electricity mains hit: supply was two-thirds back to normal next day.

Water not badly disrupted.

Traffic picked its way through streets with difficulty.

Danger of unexploded bombs.

Several hundred military and county police were drafted to Exeter to assist.

Many dead were buried at Higher Cemetery, Hamlin Lane.

Previous Raids

The raid on 3/4 May 1942 was the completion of Exeter's destruction by the Nazis.

Raids started on 24 April, when five were killed, twenty-one injured in Okehampton Road area.

The following night, 25 April (minor blitz), seventy-four killed and 100 injured in Paris Street area.

On 26 April, four killed, fifteen injured in Portland St and Newtown area. This was not all, for on 30 December 1942, in a daylight raid on the Holloway Street and St Loyes areas, eighteen died and ninety-seven were injured.

Conclusion

Altogether Exeter suffered nineteen raids, with 265 citizens killed, 111 seriously injured, 677 injured to a lesser extent.

The Germans destroyed 30 acres of built-up area, and three-quarters of the principal shopping quarter of the city.

The main areas of devastation in the city were:

High Street area (St Stephen's Church to Eastgate, and City Library to Southernhay).

Fore Street area (High Street to Coombe Street, and Cathedral Yard to Market Street).

Sidwell Street area (St Sidwell's Church to Belmont Road, Acland Terrace (now Road) to Clifton Road/Parr Street area).

In 1946 Exeter City Council approved a plan for rebuilding. It was eight years after the raids before the rebuilding commenced, for it was in 1950 that work on the laying of sewers began, and a modest start was made on construction. A very extensive, concentrated programme of redevelopment of roads and buildings was to follow in the ensuing fifteen years or so.

Looking towards the Cathedral across Catherine Street and Bampfylde Street, after the blitz

Dix's Field, 1942